HELP!
I'M A
DETECTIVE

Praise for

# Help! I'm an Alien

'[A] crazy, hilarious adventure [and]
one of the most entertaining books you
will read this year.'
*Lancashire Evening Post*

'This is a fast-paced page turner
with a laugh on every page.'
*Goodreads*

'Very impressive writing in one of the funniest
opening chapters that I've read this year.'
*The Bookbag*

'Daniel is a funny character, self-aware [and]
the pace of the narrative is perfectly pitched
to keep the reader interested
and entertained.'
*The Book Activist*

JO FRANKLIN

Illustrated
by Aaron Blecha

troika

*For Eleanor and Cedric*

First published in the UK by TROIKA BOOKS
Well House, Green Lane, Ardleigh CO7 7PD, UK
www.troikabooks.com

First published 2018



A CIP catalogue record for this book is available
from the British Library

ISBN 978-1-909991-538
1 2 3 4 5 6 7 8 9 10

Printed in Poland

# The One in the Middle

There are three children in my family. My incredibly annoying sister Jessie is the eldest and my cute baby brother Timmy is the youngest. That leaves me, Daniel (or Dan), stuck in the middle.

Jessie thinks she is the most important person in our family, the world and the whole universe. As far as she is concerned she is Number One of everything. Especially our family.

Timmy is the baby so he gets exactly what he wants all the time and no one ever tells him off. He's treated like a cross between a little prince and a favourite teddy. If Jessie is Number One in our family, then Prince Timmy is Number Two. Which means that I have been skipped over, forgotten, with no number at all.

I am nothing. A big, tall, skinny zero.

Because I am a great big nothing, I tend to get the blame for everything, even when it's not my fault.

I didn't force Jessie to stub her toe against my skateboard. It's covered in neon grip tape and fluorescent skull stickers. Any normal person would have seen it in the middle of the hallway, but Jessie never looks where she is going because her eyes are permanently glued to her phone.

In addition, I didn't make Timmy copy me when I spat out some broccoli that Mum had hidden in the chicken pie.

I admit, I do make mistakes sometimes.

I used Dad's wallet for juggling practice in the bathroom and forgot to close the toilet seat.

I mixed up the salt and sugar after a science experiment, but Mum didn't realise when she made cookies for the school fête. Her salty cookies made everyone puke.

I borrowed the screws from Mr Pitdown's chair for an art project and forgot to return them.

I got the blame for all these things and then they all got muddled up and I got the blame for that as well.

Mr Pitdown got a sore bum when he crashed to the floor.

He wrote to Mum to complain.

Mum tried to cheer him up with some of her horrid cookies.

Dad didn't have any dry money to put in the teachers' Christmas present collection, so he only put in a damp pound coin.

Mr Pitdown wasn't impressed with either of my parents' gifts.

End result: I am zero in class as well as at home.

This morning, I'd eaten my breakfast, brushed my teeth, stuffed my homework in my school bag and was about to leave for school on time. If Jessie had done this, Dad would have called the national newspapers to report a miracle. If it had been Timmy, Mum would have stuck four stars on his reward chart.

I didn't get anything. Mum and Dad didn't even notice.

Not only do I get the blame for things I haven't done, I never get rewards for things I have done.

I was about to leave the house when Mum shouted, 'Dan, what have you done with the stapler?'

'I haven't touched the stapler,' I shouted back. I had to shout because Timmy was making a racket bashing a toy on the table.

'Jessie, do you know where the stapler's gone?'

'What would I want with a stupid stapler?'

'To fix two pieces of paper together,' I said.

'I don't do paper. And I don't do staplers. I'm digital.' Jessie made a rude sign and plugged in her earphones so she could get her One Dimension fix before school.

'Rob, stapler?' Mum hadn't given up yet.

'I thought my name was Rob Kendal,' Dad said.

'Not funny!' Mum looks just like Jessie when she's angry.

'WHERE IS THE STAPLER?'

'Ape-ler. Ape-ler.' Timmy smashed his toy so hard on the table his cup tipped over and orange juice spilt across the table.

Mum grabbed the nearest thing to mop up the mess.

'That's my newspaper!' Dad said.

'It's an emergency,' Mum said.

But it was too late. The juicy wave raced across the table and over the edge, straight into Jessie's lap.

'Aarghh!' She leapt up, flipping her skirt away from her. More orange juice splashed onto the floor. 'I'm going to kill you, Daniel Kendal!'

'What did I do?' I said as everyone went berserk around me.

'The paper's ruined and now I can't do the crossword, or check yesterday's clues.' Dad held up the dripping mess and looked right at me.

'It was Timmy's fault,' I said. 'If he hadn't bashed that . . .' I pointed to the toy in Timmy's hand. Only it wasn't a toy. 'I think that's what you're looking for, Mum.' I pointed to the stapler in Timmy's hand.

'Aarghh!' Mum screamed in a perfect imitation of Jessie. 'Why didn't you tell me the baby had the stapler? Honestly, Dan, you need to take more responsibility now you're older.' Mum flipped the stapler open. 'It's fully loaded. He could have hurt himself.' She squeezed it and a staple flew out in my direction.

I ducked to avoid being stapled to death by my own mother and at exactly the same moment, I saw a flash of neon drive by the window. One of our neighbours must have called the emergency services, but I didn't know whether it was the police, fire brigade or an ambulance. I didn't care. Any of them could rescue me from my family.

Jessie must have seen it too. 'That's the police. They've come to arrest you,' she said. 'For being the most insignificant brother that ever existed. They are going to take you away and lock you up forever!'

'I haven't done anything and I'm not insignificant!'

'You are a zilch, nada, zero!' Jessie poked her tongue out at me.

Timmy wailed.

'You've made the baby cry, Dan!' Mum pulled

Timmy out of his high chair and gave him a hug.

'No, I didn't!' I felt tears well up in my own eyes but Mum didn't notice. I get the blame for EVERYTHING even when I haven't done ANYTHING.

'I'm going to school.' I slung my school bag over my shoulder and went out into the hall, but before I could open the front door, the doorbell rang.

I'm not allowed to answer the door on my own after a nasty experience we had with some alien abductee nutters a few months ago, so I had to wait while Dad pushed past me and opened the door.

This was turning into the worst day of my life ever. Jessie was right.

It was the police.

# 2 The Problem with the Police

Even though I hadn't done anything wrong, I felt guilty. It's a natural reaction when you see two police officers standing on the doorstep and your family have done nothing but blame you all morning.

The police totally ignored me as the taller officer spoke to Dad.

'Excuse me, sir, we were in the area when we heard a lot of shouting. Is there a problem here?'

'Sorry about that.' Dad blushed. 'A little family argument over breakfast.'

It wasn't a little family argument at all. It was a serious miscarriage of justice. I had been blamed for a zillion things that weren't my fault but I decided to keep quiet for now in case the police believed Dad instead of me. I was supposed to be going to school this morning, not jail.

'Would you mind asking all your family to step into the hall?' the tall officer said.

I think he was playing 'bad cop'. The other officer was a woman. She smiled at me as if she was 'good cop'. But I've seen so many police programmes that I know the 'good cop' is only pretending to be nice to trick the suspect, so I didn't smile back.

Dad called to Mum and Jessie to join us.

Bad Cop continued. 'There has been a burglary in the area. Did anyone notice anything unusual last night?'

We all shook our heads.

'Another one?' Dad said. 'Who's been broken into this time?'

'Miss Duffy,' Bad Cop said.

'Carol? I better go and see if she is okay.' Dad grabbed his coat.

'You need to take Jessie to school,' Mum said to him in her own Bad Cop voice. Mum doesn't like Carol. Dad does. 'We didn't see or hear anything, officer. Do you mind if we get the kids off to school?'

Bad Cop looked me up and down as if he was inspecting me for clues but nodded and let me walk away while he and Good Cop moved onto the next house.

I went off to school with my head down and my hood up. I wanted to remain anonymous. I had three books overdue from the library, which Mum said was a very serious crime.

This morning all the neighbours were standing at their front gates or peering round their curtains. It felt like they were looking at me even though I was trying not to be seen. I'm not used to that much attention. I don't know why they were interested in me all of a sudden. I wasn't the burglar. I'd been asleep in my loft bed all night, not creeping around their houses taking stuff that didn't belong to me. Didn't they realise I was a zilch, nada, zero?

Freddo and Gordon were already in the classroom when I walked in. They are my two best friends but they ignore each other when I'm not there.

Gordon was sitting at his desk in the front row talking to his laptop. He is the only person allowed to have a laptop in class. It's not because he's got dyslexia or bad handwriting – he's the neatest kid in the class (in the world, probably) – but he gets the shakes if he puts his laptop away so the teachers let him keep it with him, so long as he closes the lid during lessons.

Freddo was sitting at his desk (next to mine), digging the crud out of his fingernails with the point of his compass.

Is there a word that means the complete opposite of identical twins? Identical twins are so like each other that no one can tell them apart. My two best friends are so completely different from each other, the only thing they have in common is me.

'Dan, my man!' Freddo held up his hand for a high five. He still had his compass in his hand and as I didn't want to be stabbed I waved vaguely and collapsed onto my seat. Gordon didn't say anything but I could see the muscles twitching by his ears so I knew he was only pretending to ignore me.

'What's occurring?' Freddo said.

'Usual,' I said. 'I am being blamed for everything including the end of the world, and there was a burglary in our street last night. No one has tried to pin it on me yet, but give them time.'

'Cool!' Freddo said. 'What was taken?'

'I don't know. Usual stuff – TV, phones, computers, I guess.'

Gordon pulled his laptop closer to him and gave it a protective stroke.

'The place was crawling with police. Hopefully they'll catch them before they strike again,' I said.

'Twenty-three point three per cent,' Gordon said.

Freddo rolled his eyes at me.

'What's that, Gordon?' I said.

'There are over one million burglaries a year in this country and only twenty-three point three per cent are solved.'

'Is that all?' I said. Gordon was always coming up with weird statistics. I ignored him most of the time. Freddo ignored him all of the time. But this was really serious. A crime had been committed in my street. 'Are you saying the police probably won't catch the burglars?'

Gordon nodded and carried on typing.

'It'll be the same gang,' Freddo said as he continued excavating his nails. 'They can often strike in the same neighbourhood. They won't stop until they're caught.' He wiped the compass point on the edge of the desk, adding his nail crud to his dried bogey collection.

'But why can't they catch them?' I said. A panic started bubbling up inside me. I didn't want the burglars coming to my house while I was at school. I'd left my games console on my bed. And I'd got £26.73 saved up. It was locked in my money box, but if a burglar could open the front door, they'd easily be able to break open a plastic safe from the pound shop. 'They always catch the criminal on *CSI*.'

'*Crime Scene Investigations* is an American television programme, Mr Kendal.' Gordon looked at me as if I was a total idiot. 'It isn't real.'

'I know that, but we have crime scenes over here and we have investigators, don't we? What do you call them . . . forensics?'

'I calculate that if our police force used all the techniques employed on CSI they would solve ninety-five per cent of all burglaries,' Gordon said.

'What's stopping them?' I wondered if I could sneak out at break time, rush back home and hide all my stuff.

'No money. Cuts, innit.' Freddo transferred some of his nail crud and dried bogies onto a crisp and stuffed it in his mouth.

'It rained last night,' Gordon said. 'The usual methods of fingerprint recognition probably won't work.'

'How do you know these things?' Freddo said.

Gordon looked up for a moment, both eyes

focused on the bridge of his glasses. He coughed sharply and his eyes sprung back so he looked vaguely normal again.

'I am making a study of the degradation of fingerprint evidence,' he said.

'What's that in English?' Freddo said.

'I am running a series of experiments to see how long fingerprints last and I am developing new methods for detecting them.'

'Why?' Freddo thought Gordon's whacko experiments were a waste of time.

Gordon didn't answer.

'But that's brilliant,' I said. 'You could help the police catch the burglars.'

'No, I could not,' Gordon said. 'I'm not old enough. You have to be eighteen to join the police force in this country.'

'You don't have to become a full-blown police officer, but you could help them.' I leant forward, trying to look Gordon in the eye.

Gordon frowned a little and shifted his chair away from me before he went back to his laptop.

'Look, mate, I need you. It could be my house next or another round here – your street, maybe.'

I've never been to Gordon's house but I'd bet it is a burglar's paradise. Gordon had the very latest model of every electronic device on the planet. His house probably had more tech in it than the Apple store and PC World combined.

Gordon didn't stop typing but my phone bleeped. I'd received a text message.

> Meet at your house 17.00 tonight and don't call me mate.

Gordon didn't think I was a zero. I was his ~~mate~~ friend, even if he couldn't say it to my face.

# The Three Detectives

The doorbell rang at exactly five o'clock. That's 17.00 in Gordon-speak. His watch is linked to Greenwich so he is never late. His absolute punctuality meant that I felt confident opening the door without adult supervision. Gordon had changed out of his school clothes and into a police-issue paper onesie.

'What are you wearing that for?' I said.

'I don't want to contaminate the crime scene.'

'The crime scene is over there,' I pointed out number twenty-eight, 'not here. Yet.'

A mini motorcycle buzzed around the corner. It was Freddo.

'What's occurring?' he said. His new catchphrase

was beginning to annoy me.

'Your arrest in five minutes,' I said. 'Aren't those motorbikes illegal on the road?'

'That's why I was on the pavement,' Freddo said, missing my point. 'And anyway, where are the cops?' He was right. The police had gone home. 'Where's Gordon?'

I pointed at the living, breathing paper suit.

Freddo raised his eyebrows. 'I thought that was a toilet roll.'

A crackle of annoyance rippled through Gordon's paper onesie.

'I think you better hide that.' I pointed to the semi-legal motorbike. 'In case the police come back.'

'Can I stick it inside?' Freddo said. He didn't wait for an answer. He hauled his bike through the door, shoved my skateboard out of the way and dumped his motorbike in our hallway. One of the tyres was covered in mud. At least, I think it was mud.

We have to take our shoes off in the house. I didn't know what the rules were for motorbikes, but I could guess. I dragged Freddo outside before Mum came and told him to move it.

'I have . . . ahem . . . obtained the details of the houses that have been broken into in the last few months,' Gordon said. 'Which were the last to be burgled?'

I wasn't sure if Gordon had hacked into the police computer or been reading the local newspaper, but I didn't like to ask. I pointed to number twenty-eight and thirty-two. 'They got in round the back.'

Gordon took out a map of our street. On my side

of the street, the houses are in pairs with a gate on one side that lets you into the back garden. On the other side of the road, the houses are joined up in a row and they have an alleyway running all the way along the back of the houses.

'I want to examine the rear of number thirty,' Gordon said. 'I want to know why the burglars didn't break in there.' Gordon picked up his case.

'What have you got in the case, mate?' Freddo said.

Gordon ignored him and stepped to the side of

the pavement. He looked left. Looked right. Looked left again. There was no traffic in sight, but Gordon didn't cross the road. He looked left again, right again, left again, but still didn't cross.

'What's the matter with him?' Freddo said.

'He's doing the Green Cross Code,' I said. 'You know – stop, look and listen before crossing the road safely.'

'There's nothing coming,' Freddo whispered to me.

I shrugged. 'You know Gordon.'

Gordon looked for traffic again before rustling across the road. His paper suit would be hopeless if he was trying to sneak about unnoticed.

I nudged Freddo. 'Don't call him "mate".'

'But it's my new catchphrase, mate.'

'I know!' I said. 'But Gordon doesn't like it.'

'What do I call him then?'

'Gordon?' I suggested.

Freddo shrugged and we followed our crime-scene-investigator friend across the road and into the alleyway at the back of the houses. Normally it is totally overgrown with weeds, but today the weeds were smashed down in places.

'The police have looked here and here.' Gordon

pointed to the trampled patches behind two of the houses. 'But this area behind number thirty is still overgrown.' He took out a magnifying glass and examined the nettles. 'This plant is bruised at the top but has not wilted. I therefore deduce that someone with . . .' He stopped for a moment, fumbled in his case and took out a tape measure. '. . . size ten feet attempted to break in here last night and something prevented him from going any further.'

'This wouldn't have stopped them.' Freddo leant over and rattled the fence. 'It's falling apart.'

'Grrowwwoofff!' A huge wolf leapt up from behind the fence and nearly ripped Freddo's hand off.

'Arghhh!' Freddo fell back, grabbed me and pulled me in front of him like a human shield.

A mouth full of teeth kept appearing and disappearing over the fence as the rabid wolf tried to get us.

'Its teeth are already dripping with blood!' Freddo gripped me so tightly, I couldn't breathe. 'I think it's a werewolf!'

I couldn't see any blood, but the creature was getting more and more frenzied. It looked very hungry and if it got over that fence we would be its next meal. 'Let's get out of here!'

Freddo let go of me and we legged it down the alley and back to the road, leaving the rabid werewolf to hurl itself at the fence. We didn't stop until we got to my doorstep.

'Did you see its eyes?' Freddo panted. 'They were fluorescent green.'

'You're right, that thing was radioactive and it was so massive it could have snapped my arm in two. I guess that answers the question, Gordon.' I looked around for our geeky friend. But Gordon wasn't with us. We must have left him in the alley.

Everything was silent except for the blood-curdling yells of the monster tearing our friend apart behind the houses on the other side of the street.

We had left him to be eaten alive.

'We've got to help him.' I looked at Freddo, hoping he was with me.

'No way! He never helps me out!'

'He's helped me,' I said. 'Loads of times.'

The barking seemed to be getting worse.

'He'll be all right.' Freddo shrugged. 'He's wearing his protective onesie.'

'It's made of paper! It won't save him from that monster. He's going to be eaten alive. Call an ambulance!' And then I ran. I didn't care if Freddo was with me or not. I had to save Gordon.

As I hurtled down the alley, I scanned the scene ahead, preparing myself for the worst. I expected to see blood, brains and a pair of chewed glasses. But for once, luck was on our side. The nuclear werewolf had not escaped.

A quaking statue wearing a flimsy paper suit stood in the middle of the alley. Gordon stared ahead but I don't think he saw anything. He was in a terrified trance.

'Lucy!' A shrill voice rang out from number thirty. The dog hesitated for a second, poised at a large hole in the fence. I could see its head clearly for the first time. It had white fluffy fur and looked a bit like a poodle (an über-fierce one). A woman called out 'Lucy' again but the dog barked louder than ever and carried on trying to rip the fence down.

A hand heavy with gold rings grabbed the dog and hauled it back into the garden. 'What you barking at?'

Yikes! The owner was going to let a half-starved, fully rabid, radioactive werewolf-poodle out to get us! I needed to wake Gordon from his trance so that we could run for it. There was only one word that was going to force a reaction.

'Mate! We've got to move! Right now, mate!'

Gordon blinked. His body switched from terrified statue to fuming demon. His eyeballs bulged and he took a swipe at me with his magnifying glass.

'Run!' I grabbed his silver case and dashed down the alley. Gordon said something which might have been rude but he followed me anyway. We didn't stop until we were at my house and I had slammed the garden gate behind us.

'Did it get you?' Freddo said, putting down his phone.

I shook my head. 'Did you call the ambulance?' I panted.

'Nah,' Freddo said. 'I was on the phone to my mum. She wants me to stop at the chippie on the way back. Can you let me in so I can get my bike?'

Typical! Gordon and I might have had our legs ripped off and Freddo was thinking of chips. Sometimes he is a rubbish best friend. I opened the front door without saying a word. A disgusting smell wafted out.

Freddo grabbed his mini motorbike and wheeled it down the path leaving brown tyre marks behind him. He hopped onto his bike and sped off to his chip dinner. 'See you tomorrow, mates!'

Sometimes I really wonder why I am still friends with him. He'd gone home even though we were no closer to catching the burglars. But Gordon, who is officially only my second best friend, was still here with me. I think that was the most exercise he had done in his life. His face was a little red but he was breathing normally now.

'Our lives may have been in danger but I was able to deduce one thing.' Gordon snapped open his silver case, took out his laptop and tapped into it.

'What's that then? That it wasn't mud on Freddo's tyres?' I said, wrinkling my nose. My front hallway now stank of dog poo.

Gordon looked over his glasses and frowned. 'We now know how to protect you and your family from getting burgled.'

I looked at him blankly.

'You need to get a dog.'

# The Problem with Dogs

We don't have any pets. Mum says four dependents (she means us three children plus Dad) are more than enough.

Before Timmy was born, I used to enjoy visiting the rabbits and guinea pigs at the pet shop. But now I grab hold of my baby brother if I want to cuddle something cute.

Dad says we already live in a zoo. I'm not sure which animals he thinks we are.

Timmy would be something cute and cuddly, Jessie would have to be a screeching maniac and I'd be something with ridiculously long legs, but hopefully not an octopus as I don't like swimming.

So, I figured it was going to be pretty difficult to persuade my parents that we really needed a dog.

'What is that terrible smell?' Mum said to me the minute I came into the hallway after Freddo and Gordon had gone home. 'Have you stepped in something?'

'No, I haven't,' I said truthfully but I moved

down the hall to take Mum's focus away from the large brown skid mark left by Freddo's bike.

Jessie stomped downstairs, dressed to go out. She stopped halfway down.

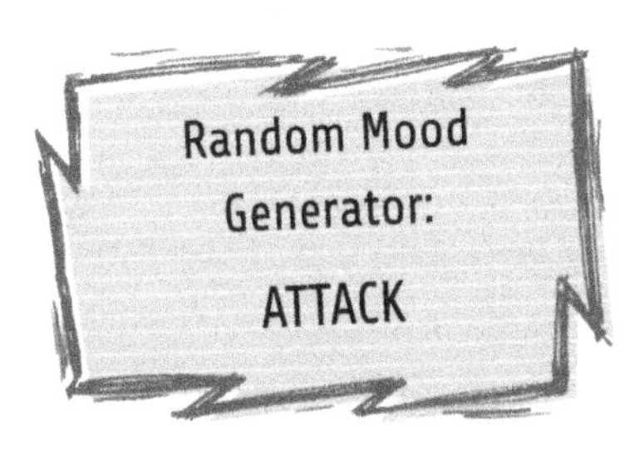


'Poo, you stink!' she said.

'I don't stink!' I said. 'Anyway, you smell of something weird!' I said. I think Jessie was wearing perfume.

'Argani Rose, body spray. Dazzer bought it for me,' she said.

'It stinks!' I said.

'It smells lovely!' Jessie shouted.

'Have you done your homework, Jessie?' Mum said. I couldn't tell if she didn't like Jessie's perfume or whether she didn't like Jessie going out with Dazzer again, but she was annoyed about something.

'Yes, I have.' Jessie switched her Random Mood Generator.

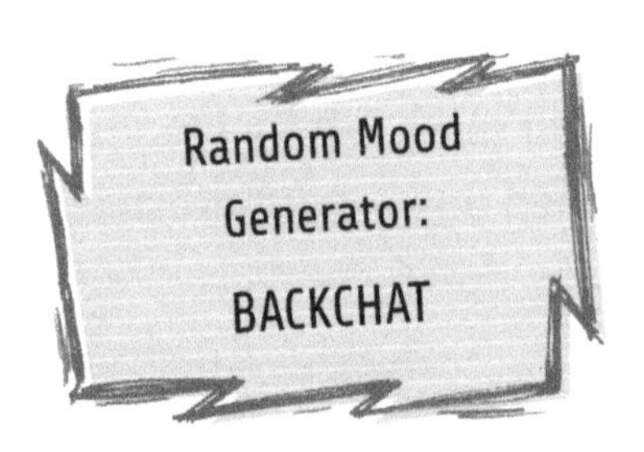


'And before you ask, yes, I do have my key and I won't be late.'

Jessie was busy being so rude that she didn't look where she was going. She stepped off the bottom stair and straight onto my skateboard that Freddo had moved to make way for his bike.

Jessie shot forward, her hair, arms and legs sticking out in all directions.

'Aarghh!' she screamed as she hurtled towards me. I bent my knees to brace myself for impact and grabbed her round the middle as she smacked into me.

'Get off! I don't want some skunk brother touching me!' She pushed me out the way, kicked my skateboard and stormed out of the front door.

'I don't stink!' I said. Which is true. I don't smell too bad at all.

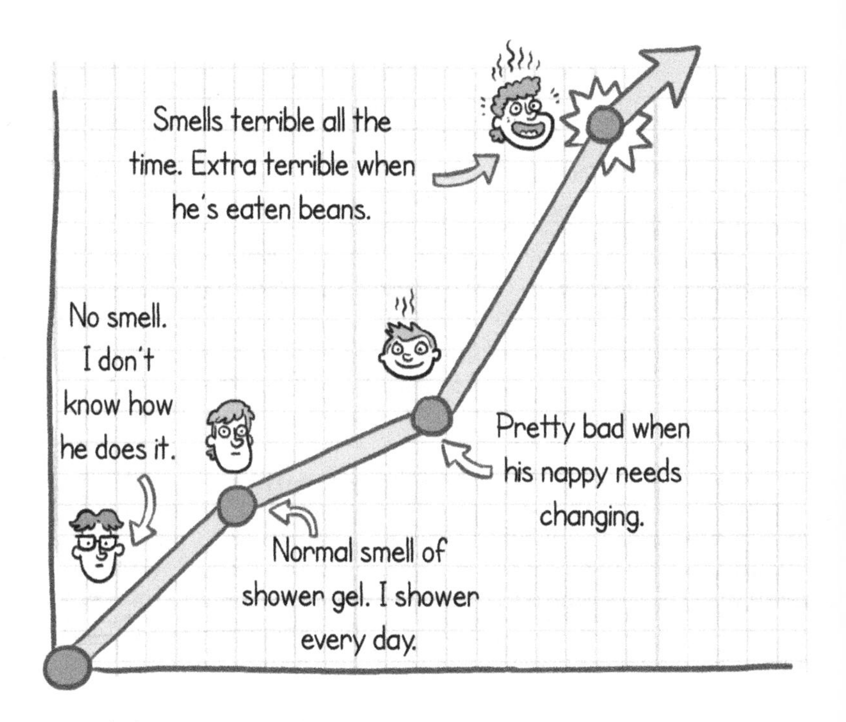


I didn't want to be a zilch, nada, zero or a skunk. But I was talking to myself. Jessie had gone, slamming the door behind her.

Dad poked his head round the kitchen door.

'What was all that screaming?'

'Jessie tripped over Dan's skateboard,' Mum said.

'I told you not to leave that skateboard lying around, Dan,' Dad said. He grabbed the skateboard and shoved it in the cupboard under the stairs. 'No skateboard for a week.'

I got the blame again. I didn't bother arguing, I had something more important to discuss.

'I was thinking,' I said, 'if we got a dog, it would put the burglars off.'

'We are not getting a dog,' Mum said.

'Burglars won't break in if a dog barks,' I said.

'We're not getting a dog,' Dad said. 'And what is that disgusting smell?'

'Smells like dog poo.' Mum sniffed. 'That's why I hate dogs. They poo everywhere and the pavements are covered in it.'

'What's that?' Dad pointed to the brown tyre print on the carpet.

I didn't say anything, but there must have been something about the way I was silent because Mum and Dad both turned to look at me at exactly the same time, expecting an answer.

'Freddo put his bike there,' I said.

'He brought his bicycle into the house?' Mum said.

'Not his bicycle. His motorbike.'

'What?' Mum's own Random Mood Generator switched from WEARY to VESUVIUS. 'He brought a vehicle from the road onto my carpet?'

'He didn't go on the road. He went on the pavement.'

'Is that the dog-poo-covered pavement we were just talking about?' Mum said.

And I guess that's when I knew there was no way Mum and Dad would agree to me getting a dog.

'If we're not getting a dog, I think I better stay home tomorrow,' I said, 'so I can guard the house.'

'You are going to school. We are going to work. We are not going to be burgled,' Dad said. 'Mum has fitted a new lock on the back door. The house is secure.'

'Get scrubbing!' Mum handed me a bottle of carpet shampoo and pointed to the dirty mark on the carpet.

That was the end of the 'can we have a dog' conversation.

# My Little Pony - Not!

I wasn't sure if it was the smell of carpet cleaner mixed with Freddo's dog poo skid mark or the worry of being burgled that kept me awake all night, but I didn't get much sleep. Mum and Dad might have thought that we weren't going to be robbed but I was convinced the burglars were coming to get us and I didn't want my stuff to be stolen.

At three in the morning, I decided to turn the den under my loft bed into a fortress. It was the perfect place to hide everything important and I could set up some sort of defence mechanism so the burglars couldn't get my stuff, even if they got into the house.

In the morning, I gulped down my breakfast, threw my clothes on and started work.

I opened my cupboard and took out everything that had special value to me.

Wow! I had some really important stuff to protect.

Two sets of Mousetrap that never worked.

A wooden Thomas the Tank Engine that I had decided to keep for myself even though I had given the rest of my wooden railway to Timmy.

Seventeen cuddly toys that I usually kept hidden from Freddo.

I crammed them all under my bed.

But I kept finding more really important stuff that I had forgotten about.

A bag full of small tubs of slime that Mum had bought for party bags one year but had forgotten about.

A pink rubber My Little Pony with a purple mane.

STOP!

REWIND!

What was that doing in my room? It wasn't mine! The burglars could have it.

I slung the Not My Little Pony out onto the landing but the stupid thing bounced back into my room, knocking over a pot of marbles, which spilt all over the floor.

Arghh! I didn't have time to tidy them up now. I rolled them under the chest of drawers so Mum couldn't see them. If she finds stuff lying around on the floor it goes straight in a bag and is taken down to the charity shop. Especially if the stuff belongs to me. This is one of her most annoying habits and is the reason why I had to make certain that the really important stuff was IN my den, but NOT touching the carpet. I didn't want the burglars stealing it, but I didn't want Mum giving it away either.

I was trying to find a place for my last few treasures when my feet suddenly shot out from under me. I tried to grab the ladder to my bed but I was moving too quickly in the opposite direction. Now I knew how Jessie felt when she stepped on my skateboard. My feet were moving forward but my body couldn't keep up and my bum thumped down into a cardboard box. A blue cat's-eye marble rolled from under my feet. I pulled myself out of the box and had a quick look round to make sure no one had seen me making such an idiot of myself.

'You nearly killed me!' I kicked the marble under the chest of drawers. 'Stay there with your stupid glassy friends!'

The squashed box contained a load of electronics, including my old Nintendo DS. I hadn't played it in years but I didn't want to throw it away. I pulled a few leads out of the box to see if any of them matched but they were all attached to other things I'd forgotten about.

'Dan, time for school!' Dad shouted from downstairs. He was as loud as any dog. Shame I couldn't set him to bark if a burglar showed up.

And that's when I had my brilliant idea.

I bundled up a few essentials from my box of vintage electronics and stuffed them in my school bag.

The Not My Little Pony lay on its side in my doorway. It had never been mine. It was Jessie's. Maybe if I gave it back to her, she wouldn't think I was insignificant any more.

'I think you've lost something,' I said as I opened her bedroom door and tossed the hideous purple toy to her.

'Get lost, zilch-boy!' She threw it back, followed by her complete My Little Pony collection.

I was under attack! Rubber toys bounced off my head, the walls and the bannister. Each one looked

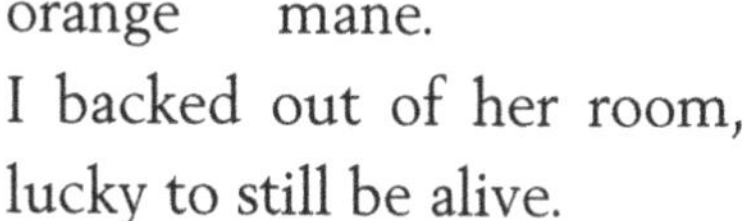

weirder than the last. Green body, yellow mane. Turquoise body, orange mane. I backed out of her room, lucky to still be alive.

I was never going to be anything but an insignificant, zero zilch-boy to Jessie. There was nothing I could do to change that.

The landing looked like a My Little Pony graveyard. Mum would go berserk when she came upstairs, but it wasn't my problem.

The only problem I had was to get my brilliant idea in place before the burglars came round.

I left the ponies on the landing and hurtled down the stairs and out the door to school.

Luckily Mr Pitdown was faffing about with the whiteboard when I got into class. I just had time to brief the mission team.

'Mum and Dad don't want a dog,' I said. 'They found dog poo in our front hall and went nuts.'

'Same thing happened at my house last night,'

Freddo said. 'Amazing coincidence.'

'I don't want to go into that now,' I said, my hands still stinging from the carpet cleaner. 'The thing is, I realised that I don't need a real dog. One with fur and poop. I only need one that barks.'

'Mate, if you get a dog that barks, it will have fur and poop as well.' Freddo scrunched his crisp packet into a ball and threw it at my head.

'Will you shut up for a moment and listen to me? I don't need a dog at all. I just need the barking. You gave me this for Christmas last year, Freddo.' I unravelled the flex from the gadget I had bought from home. 'It's a motion-triggered Nerf gun.'

'Oh yeah,' Freddo said. 'Your mum went mad because Timmy kept crawling in front of it and getting shot. Is that why she hates me?'

If I told Freddo all the reasons why Mum might hate him we'd be here for eternity.

'Could you adapt this, Gordon, so that if a burglar walked in front of it, it would set off the sound of a dog barking instead of foam bullets?'

Gordon pulled on a pair of leather gloves before taking the gadget from me.

'It may be possible,' he said, 'but it would need

some sort of music player and loudspeaker.'

I looked hopefully at Freddo. I can always rely on Freddo to come up with bits and pieces. His dad runs a market stall and has loads of lock-up garages stuffed with useful things.

'What do you want?' Freddo said. 'A CD player, an MP3 player or a digital recording device?' he said.

'I don't care,' I said. 'As long as it can play loud barking and it can be attached to the motion sensor.'

'I'll see what I can do,' Freddo said, 'but you'll have to supply the barking.'

'No problem,' I said. I knew exactly where to get that from.

# Plan A

Freddo and Gordon may be my two best friends but sometimes Mum and Dad get worried about what we are up to – ever since the day they found us trying to freeze my body alive. So I decided to tell them that my friends were coming round to 'play' rather than 'set up a burglar alarm'.

Hopefully, if I can stop the burglars, Mum and Dad will forgive me telling such a small lie. They might forgive me for a few other things too – although I don't think they will ever forgive the dog-poo incident. Jessie might even stop calling me zilch-boy if I protected her stuff from thieves.

'Freddo is never to bring that motorbike into this

house again,' Mum said when I told her that he and Gordon were dropping by after tea.

'I know,' I said.

'And I don't want you going out this evening. It's getting dark and there are ... people around.'

I didn't answer because I didn't want to tell another lie. Going outside was a crucial part of my plan. Mum usually let me play out in the street, she was only being über-cautious because of the burglars. But the burglars were after stuff they could sell – they wouldn't be interested in stealing me.

Luckily Mum didn't notice I was quiet because she was too busy talking to Jessie about her latest tap-dancing routine while feeding Timmy his tea. One of the advantages of being the zilch-nada-zero-child is that when you are not being nagged to death or blamed for everything, you are being ignored, which means no one notices if you sneak out when you have been told not to.

I heard Freddo buzzing up the pavement on his mini motorbike so I went outside to meet him.

'You have to park round the back, in the garden,' I said.

'What if it rains?'

'It'll wash the dog poo off your tyres.'

'Good thinking!' Freddo said as he wheeled his bike through our side gate. He came back to the front doorstep to show me what he had brought with him. It was a tiny handheld device, about the size of a two-finger Kit Kat. He pressed a button and a tinny tune played out.

'*Who let the dogs out? Woof! Woof! Woof! Woof!*'

'Is that it?' I said.

'It's a great song. It reached number one in Australia and it's about dogs.' He pressed the button again.

'*Who let the dogs out? Woof! Woof! Woof! Woof!*'

'It's not very loud,' I said. I realised that Freddo had gone to a lot of trouble, but I wasn't very impressed with his recording. 'Or very scary.'

'I've got these to pump up the volume.' Freddo pulled two massive speakers out of his bag. 'Surround sound and everything.'

'The speakers are great but I don't think that song will scare the burglars,' I said. 'I was thinking we could record a real dog barking.'

'Yeah?' Freddo said. I could tell by the way he looked at me he knew what dog I was talking about.

'You go ahead. I'll wait here.'

'Lucy is only a poodle,' I said.

'Poodle-werewolf, you mean. I was the one who nearly had his arm ripped off, remember?' Freddo looked at the bottom of his trainers and scraped the sole against the edge of the doorstep. Luckily there was nothing to scrape off. I think he was just trying to avoid looking at me in case I could see how scared he was.

'Her bark is worse than her bite and the bark is exactly what we need,' I said. 'Anyway, I don't know how that digital thing works.'

'Let me show you. I can give you detailed instructions.' Freddo rolled up his sleeves. 'You press the red button to start recording and press it again to stop. Simples!'

'I think it would be better if you came with me,' I said.

Freddo didn't agree.

In the end I had to bribe him. His price was three packets of crisps every day for one week. The crisps had to be his favourite brand, not the ones Mum usually buys from the discount supermarket. Being friends with Freddo was getting very expensive but

I didn't want to walk into the jaws of the werepoodle on my own.

It was nearly dark by the time we'd made the deal. We needed to make our recording before Gordon showed up. If he rang the doorbell, Mum would give me a shout, realise that Freddo and I were NOT upstairs playing Monopoly and my friends would probably be banned again.

I zipped up my hoodie to the throat and pulled the hood over my head and right down to my eyebrows, hoping it would make me anonymous, and led the way across the road. There was no one else around. Everyone who lived on Beechwood Road was safely behind their locked doors, guarding their stuff. Freddo and I were the only ones on a life-threatening mission.

I had only seen Lucy briefly as she growled over the fence to bark at us. I'd told Freddo she was a poodle to make her seem less of a menace, but I didn't really know what breed of dog she was.

There were no street lights in the alley. The sky was that weird grey-purple that makes everything shadowy and unreal. The outline of the bare trees looked more like witches' broomsticks than living things.

'Wish I'd bought my torch,' I muttered.

Freddo stopped walking. I couldn't see his face but I sensed his fear. It was the same as mine.

'Come on,' I whispered. I strode down the alleyway in a perfect imitation of someone who wasn't scared and stopped at the back of the dog's house.

Freddo shuffled behind me. I wanted to hold his hand.

STOP!

REWIND!

What I mean is, I wanted some reassurance that he was with me.

**Pppppffffffffttttt!**

A very familiar sound and smell came from Freddo's bum. He was there all right!

'This is not the time!' I shouted.

'Grrowwwoofff!' Lucy leapt to life over the other side of the fence. I jumped three metres into the air and Freddo practically threw himself into my arms. 'Grrr! Woof! Woof! Woof!'

Freddo and I clung to each other like a couple of limpets-in-love until Lucy was silent again.

'Did you get it?' I hissed.

'What?' Freddo said.

'The recording of her barking!'

'No!'

'You are in charge of the red button!' I pushed my useless best friend away. 'We'll have to get her barking again.'

'Go on then.' Freddo held the digital recorder

to my face and pressed the red button. Then he jabbed his finger first at me then at the fence. He didn't have to say anything. I knew what I had to do.

I took a step closer to the home of the werepoodle. 'You better be recording, mate,' I said under my breath, then grabbed the fence and gave it a rattle.

Lucy erupted into a frenzy AND six industrial floodlights lit up the alleyway. Lucy's owners must have set them up to come on if anyone tried to climb the fence.

'Who's there?' a voice yelled out. It was a man this time and he sounded pretty mean. 'I'm going to get you!'

He didn't have to say it twice. I ran like mad and Freddo raced behind me. We skidded out of the alley, into Beechwood Road and back home. Shame it wasn't the Olympics. We would have beaten Usain Bolt for sure.

Gordon was at the front door. He was about to ring the bell but had to step back as Freddo and I hurtled down the path. For once our timing was perfect. I slammed the front gate shut. We had got back home without being eaten alive by the werepoodle and without Mum even knowing I'd been out.

'Got the recording?' I said to Freddo.

Freddo was panting so hard he couldn't speak, but he seemed to be nodding his head.

'We're ready for you, Gordon,' I said.

Gordon isn't called The Geek for nothing. Within two minutes he had assembled a motion-controlled Barker, all without leaving my doorstep.

'Are you sure it isn't going to poop?' I said.

'This is an electronic device. It has no digestive tract, Mr Kendal.' Gordon calls me Mr Kendal to let me know when he thinks I'm a total moron. He doesn't realise I say stupid things on purpose because I know he gets a kick out of making me feel like an idiot. I think it's the only reason he's friends with me – so he can feel even brainer than he already is.

The front door opened. It was Jessie, buttoning up her coat.

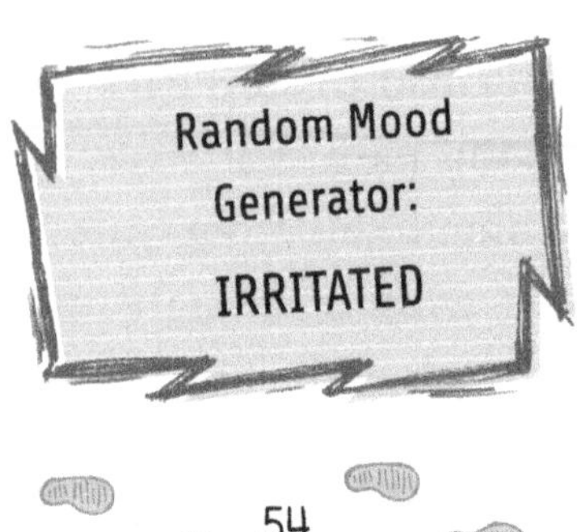

'What are you and your freaky friends doing now?'

Gordon snapped the locks on his briefcase shut and left without saying a word. He doesn't mind being called The Geek, but he hates the word 'freak' almost as much as he hates 'mate'.

I hate being called a freak too, but I have to put up with it because Jessie is part of my family and I'm too young to leave home.

'None of your business,' I said and stood in front of the Barker so she couldn't see it.

'Mum thinks you're upstairs. She'll go mental if she knows you're out here, and if she goes mental she might stop me going out.'

'And that'll be my fault, I suppose?'

'Everything is your fault, haven't you realised that, you moronic nobody?' She slammed her hands on her hips and jutted her face so close to me I thought she was going to rip my eyebrows off with her teeth.

'Hi, Jessie,' Freddo said and he gave Jessie a little wave. He didn't seem to mind being called a freak. In fact, I think he liked it. He smiled at Jessie like he'd never smiled at me.

'You want something?' Jessie said.

‘I was just saying “hi”,’ Freddo said. ‘Nice shoes. Going anywhere special?’

Nice shoes?! I hadn’t even realised Jessie was wearing shoes!

Jessie’s Random Mood Generator suddenly switched to something I’ve never seen before. A cross between FLATTERED and MESMERISED.

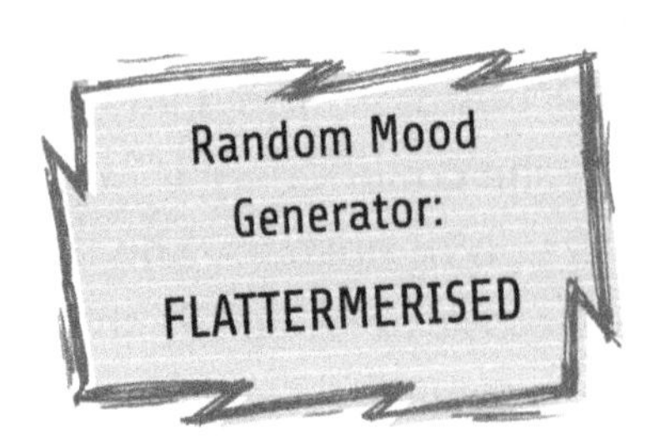


‘I’m going out with my boyfriend,’ she said, and rearranged a few strands of hair over her ears.

‘Have a nice time.’ Freddo smiled his crazy hypnotising smile again.

‘Thanks,’ Jessie mumbled. She stepped over the Barker and walked down the street, glancing over her shoulder at Freddo as she went.

‘How did you do that?’ I said. ‘You tamed Jessie!’

Freddo smiled, shrugged, and then let rip one of his hideous farts before disappearing through the side gate to get his motorcycle. He started the engine and wheeled his way along our narrow path back to the road.

'I thought you were saving your farts to power your bike,' I said. 'Wasn't Gordon going to convert the engine to methane?'

'Gordon complained about the quality of the gas I was producing. He told me I had to eat three cabbages a day, which isn't going to happen.' Freddo lifted his bum off the seat, let out a small trump and buzzed away down the pavement, leaving me alone with my new friend, the Barker.

# The Midnight Barker

My home – twenty-six Beechwood Road – was safe at last.

Timmy was asleep in his cot. Jessie was worshipping at her shrine to One Dimension. Mum and Dad had gone to bed early. My family didn't know it, but I was the most important person in the house right now. I was guarding them all from the safety of my own bed.

The Barker was in position. The laser beam shone across the top of the stairs. No one could get near my family or my stuff without me knowing about it. No one!

I drifted into a snuggly deep sleep.

*'WHO LET THE DOGS OUT? WOOF! WOOF! WOOF! WOOF!'*

I leapt horizontally out of bed and hit my head, knees and toes on the ceiling all at once.

*'WHO LET THE DOGS OUT? WOOF! WOOF! WOOF! WOOF!'*

Freddo's favourite tune blasted through our house.

Two thoughts entered my brain at exactly the same time.

1) The Barker was supposed to bark, not sing.

2) We were being burgled.

I stumbled out onto the landing, my head still throbbing from being smacked on the ceiling.

Mum and Dad looked around, dazed in their pyjamas.

Jessie stood on the landing too and for some reason she had her coat on.

'Turn it down, Jessie!' Dad shouted over the racket that had once been number one in Australia.

'Purr-lease,' Jessie shouted back. 'I have better taste in music than that.'

'Dan, is it your music?' Dad shouted at me.

'Not exactly,' I said.

'YOU BETTER BE RECORDING THIS.' My voice blasted out of the speakers followed by Lucy the werepoodle's ferocious barking.

'Sounds like you,' Dad shouted.

'Will you turn it off? You'll wake the baby,' Mum said.

'Wah!' Timmy started screaming.

'For goodness' sake, Daniel!' Mum said as she went to pick Timmy up.

I fumbled for the red button and turned the Barker off. Instead of barking the landing was full to the brim with anger, shock and grumpiness, interspersed by wails from Timmy.

'It's a burglar alarm,' I said. 'Someone must have come upstairs and stepped through the motion-sensitive beam.'

I waved my hand in front of the red beam that ran from the Barker across the top of the stairs.

'*WHO LET THE DOGS OUT? WOOF! WOOF! WOOF! WOOF!*' blasted out again.

'Enough!' Dad yelled. 'I was asleep. I still am, I think.' He scratched his head.

'We are being burgled!' I said as I yanked the plug out of the wall. 'Why don't you ever listen to me?'

'I don't see any burglars,' Dad said.

I opened my mouth to explain about the Barker again but I closed it quickly when I realised that Dad was right. Everyone on the landing was a member of the Kendal family. The only strange thing was that Jessie was wearing her coat, while the rest of us were in pyjamas.

'Jessie?' Mum said. 'Where have you been?'

Jessie shot me a lethal look and folded her arms across her chest. 'It's only eleven o'clock,' she said.

'I thought you came back hours ago,' Mum said. 'And it's not eleven, it's nearly midnight. And anyway it's far too late for a school night.'

That's the moment I realised the fatal flaw in the Barker. It didn't know the difference between a real burglar and an annoying sister sneaking about in the middle of the night.

'We'll talk about it in the morning,' Dad said.

'We'll talk about how long you're grounded for, Jessie!' Mum can be just like Jessie sometimes, only her current mood wasn't random at all. It was fixed on FLIPPING FURIOUS. 'And we'll talk about this contraption too!' She kicked the Barker into the corner by the airing cupboard.

As usual Mum couldn't see that I was a worthwhile addition to the family. I had been trying to help but Mum still thought I was useless. Dad was too tired to think anything.

Mum settled Timmy back in bed. Dad went to the bathroom. Jessie came over to me and whispered in her quietest, scariest voice, 'I am going to kill you!

This is all your fault!'

It wasn't my fault. I was protecting our home. But I didn't bother telling Jessie that because her Random Mood Generator was stuck.

And I needed to stay alive, at least until the burglars were caught.

# Plan B

It's very difficult sleeping when your sister is in the next room plotting your murder. By the time I did get back to sleep it was time to get up again and I was late for school.

'The Barker didn't go too well last night,' I told Freddo under my breath during registration.

'What happened, mate?' Freddo said, only Freddo can't speak quietly.

'Freddie and Daniel, stop talking!' Mr Pitdown said.

'Yes, Mr Pitdown!' we sang out in our best angel voices because our saddo teacher likes that sort of thing. It makes him feel like God or the Pope or someone else important.

Mr Pitdown carried on with the lesson. I wasn't sure if it was maths or English. They are very similar.

I scribbled something on a piece of paper and passed the note to Freddo.

Freddo replied, who gonna kill yer?

'I'll take that!' Mr Pitdown pulled the note out of my hand. 'I told you to stop speaking so you could start studying, not write notes.'

Mr Pitdown spits when he speaks, especially when he says words with an S in them. He really likes using S-words when he's telling you off. He does it on purpose.

'What isss thisss, Daniel? Pleassse ssshare it with the classs.' He handed the note to me. It was covered in spit spots.

'I am now living under a death threat,' I read out.

Everyone laughed.

'I am! My sister Jessie wants to kill me!'

Rooners began humming a funeral march and the rest of the football team joined in.

'Have you chosen your gravestone yet?' someone called out.

'Fratricide,' Gordon said. 'When a sibling kills their brother.'

Mr Pitdown clapped his hands in that annoying way teachers do to make everyone be quiet.

CLAP. CLAP. CLAPPITY. CLAP.

'Please leave your family squabbles at home, Daniel. Freddie, please sit here.' He pointed to the empty seat at the front of the class next to Gordon. It is the unofficial naughty seat in our class. Gordon never speaks to anyone during lessons, so sitting next to him is a bit like sitting alone but it looked better if the school inspectors came in. Freddo sat down and Gordon shifted as far away as he could. I don't think Freddo and Gordon will ever be good mates.

Mr Pitdown continued droning on. I looked out of the window, trying to work out how long it was until break time so the mission team could put together an action plan.

It was pretty gloomy outside. The sun hadn't come out all day and the clouds seemed be getting blacker and blacker. If it rained at break time, we'd have to stay inside. Wet Play didn't mean a massive water fight in the playground, it meant one of Mr Pitdown's boring Educational Games Tournaments.

The clouds darkened again and the classroom lights flickered.

'Oooh!' Freddo said, and before anyone else could say anything a massive lightning bolt shot out of the sky and blasted something the other side of the school fence.

BOOM!

The lights flickered and went out with a sharp crack. Gordon screamed.

CLAP. CLAP. CLAPPITY. CLAP.

No one took any notice. We all rushed to the windows.

We couldn't see anything – it was too gloomy outside – but there was a smell of burning. Everyone started asking questions. What happened? Can lightning do that? Why are the hairs on my arms standing on end? Can we go home early?

'The lightning may have blown a fuse within the electricity distribution network,' Gordon said. 'The whole town is experiencing a power cut.'

Gordon was right. Our classroom is upstairs so we get a pretty good view of the town. Every building was dark.

'I have something to tell you, Dan.' Gordon looked over his glasses. 'Please prepare yourself for bad news.'

'I'm ready,' I gulped.

'The number of burglaries increases exponentially during a power cut.'

'What's expo-thingy mean?' I asked the question, but I guess I already knew the answer.

'A lot,' Gordon said. 'Burglars will take advantage of darkness and lack of alarms and go out robbing right now.'

Sirens wailed outside, getting closer and closer. All the emergency services were on their way to the scene of the lightning strike. I reckoned the officers investigating the burglaries at Beechwood Road were with them. A freak electrical storm was more exciting than catching a few thieves. My home was totally unprotected.

'For a crime to be committed, the villain needs three things: motive, means and opportunity,' Gordon said. 'They have the motive – they want something really badly – the means – they have the tools to break in – and a power cut is the perfect opportunity.'

Means, motive and opportunity. I had never realised that crime was so scientific.

'Everyone sit down,' Mr Pitdown said. 'Talk among yourselves while I find out what is happening.'

The rest of the class ignored him and stayed at the windows. I pulled my seat over to Gordon's desk.

'This is a disaster!' I said. 'We are defo going to be burgled now.'

'What happened with the burglar alarm I constructed for you?' Gordon said.

'The Barker picked up the wrong person creeping around illegally last night,' I said. 'That wrong person was Jessie, who was sneaking in after seeing her boyfriend when she was supposed to be in bed. Mum and Dad went mental and now Jessie wants to kill me. Again.'

'Unfortunate,' Gordon said.

'Ouch-er-ooney!' Freddo said.

'Mum and Dad have now banned the Barker. Sorry, Gordon, but your invention didn't work out this time,' I said. 'We have to think of something else. We need to catch the burglars in the act.'

It was weird sitting in the classroom in half darkness. The only light came from the occasional flash of lightning, but the storm was moving off to zap the electricity supply in another town.

'Stakeout!' Freddo said. 'We can stay up all night and watch for the burglars.'

'They might be armed.' I dropped my voice to a whisper.

'Nah!' Freddo waved his hand dismissively. 'If they had a gun they would have shot that werepoodle.'

A scary coldness grabbed my neck. I didn't particularly like Lucy, but I didn't want anything horrible to happen to her. Or me.

'And anyway, I've seen *The Karate Kid,* I know all the moves.' Freddo leapt up and spun round with his leg sticking out.

'Impressive!' I lied.

'Freddie!' Mr Pitdown said in his final-warning voice. 'Please don't practise your ballet in class!'

One of the girls sniggered but I couldn't see who because it was so gloomy with the lights out. Whether Freddo's moves were rubbish karate or unimpressive ballet, they wouldn't be enough to fight off the burglars.

'I suppose if we see the burglars, we could call the police,' I said. 'They can deal with them.'

Freddo didn't say anything. His family might have a policy of avoiding the police as far as possible, but there was no way we could deal with a whole gang of burglars without backup.

'But if this power cut continues, it'll be pitch black. And even if the street lights come back on, we won't be able to see well enough in the middle of the night,' I said. 'How will we see the burglars?'

'You need night-vision goggles. They allow you to see in the dark,' Gordon said. He was tapping away at his laptop as usual. His laptop was working even though there was no mains power throughout the whole school. His battery must have been fully charged but I don't know what he was looking at as the school Wi-Fi would have gone down with the electricity. Gordon always had a technical solution to every problem.

'Cool!' Freddo and I said at the same time. Night-vision goggles are the most awesome gadget ever. The SAS use them all the time. I've seen them on TV.

'Freddo, do you have any?' I said.

'Don't even bother asking.' Freddo held up his crisp-encrusted fingers. 'Night-vision goggles are specialist geek equipment.' He nodded towards Gordon.

'Any chance you could make a couple of pairs of night-vision goggles?' I said to Gordon.

Gordon didn't look up from his laptop but a crimson blush spread across his cheekbones.

Freddo nudged me. I nudged him back.

We both knew there was something The Geek wasn't telling us.

'Gordon, do you own a pair of night-vision goggles?' I said.

Gordon's blush spread rapidly down his neck.

Busted!

I decided to go for the direct approach.

'Gordon, could we borrow your night-vision goggles for the stakeout?'

Total geek silence.

'It's going to be awesome!' Freddo punched the air. 'We can creep around in the bushes like a couple of commandos. We'll have to smear our faces with mud so that we are completely camouflaged. We'll be able to see the burglars and find out who's not cleaning up after their dog. We'll be known as the Dog Poo Detectives!'

All the colour drained from Gordon's face. Freddo knew how to tame Jessie but he was absolutely hopeless at handling Gordon the neat-freak Geek. There was no way Gordon was going to lend his goggles to us if Freddo was going to use them to look for dog poo.

'YOU are NOT touching my night-vision goggles!' Gordon pointed a quivering finger at Freddo. 'They are brand new and very expensive.'

'Keep your hair on, mate,' Freddo said.

'About the night-vision goggles, Gordon,' I said, trying to get The Geek's attention away from Freddo. 'There's a crime wave going on and —'

CLAP. CLAP. CLAPPITY. CLAP.

Gordon clapped his hands exactly like Mr

Pitdown had done. I stopped speaking.

'I will lend you my night-vision goggles, Daniel,' he said. 'But there are some conditions.'

'Whatever you want,' I said.

'You will wash your hands and eye sockets with sanitizer before using them.'

'Yes, Gordon,' I said.

'You will not use them anywhere near mud or dog waste.'

'Yes, Gordon,' I said.

'And you will NOT take Freddo with you on the stake-out.'

Freddo pushed his chair back, folded his arms across his chest and waited for me to say something.

Gordon's conditions for lending me the night-vision goggles were a total nightmare!

If I took Freddo with me on the stake-out, Gordon wouldn't let me borrow the night-vision goggles.

If I did the stake-out on my own using Gordon's goggles, Freddo would never speak to me again.

I had to choose. Freddo or Gordon?

A thick black silence descended between us and it had nothing to do with the power cut.

'Do you have a requirement to borrow my night-vision goggles tonight?' Gordon didn't take his eyes off me.

They weren't bulging out of his eye sockets this time; they were drilling into my brain. Gordon can be pretty scary sometimes.

Freddo was watching me too. He knew what a dilemma I was in. Gordon had no idea.

The lights flickered back on. The whole class groaned.

CLAP. CLAP. CLAPPITY. CLAP.

'Return to your desks for maths,' Mr Pitdown said.

The rest of the class moved back to their seats, but Gordon carried on staring, waiting for an answer. The power cut was over but I still needed to be able to see clearly in the dark. I needed those night-vision goggles.

'Have fun tonight, mate.' Freddo thumped me on the arm and muttered something like 'without me' before he plonked himself down in the seat beside Gordon.

'See you at six o'clock,' I whispered to Gordon.

He nodded and turned to face the front of the class.

I went back to my desk, leaving Freddo still sitting next to Gordon. My two best friends, who didn't like each other.

I was the one sitting alone. Freddo probably wouldn't ever want to sit next to me again and it was all my fault.

I was the worst friend ever. Maybe Jessie was right. I was a total waste of space. A zilch, nada, zero.

# Night Vision at Home

My best friend wasn't talking to me. And no one was talking to each other at home either.

Mum had grounded Jessie and confiscated her phone for two weeks.

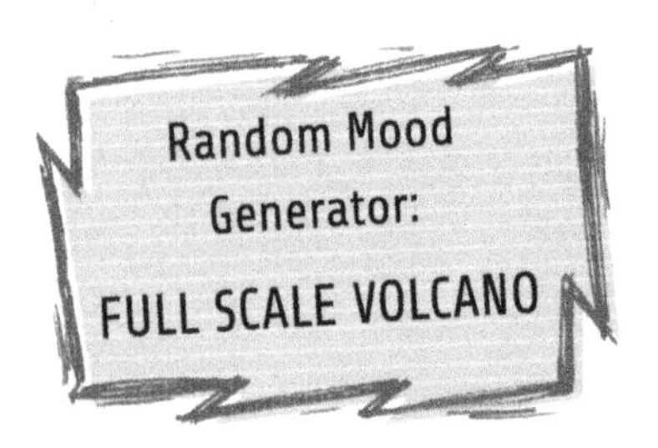


Luckily she kept to her room most of the time so we weren't all wiped out by the molten lava.

Dad didn't agree with Jessie's punishment so he wasn't talking to Mum.

Mum was so upset with Dad and Jessie, she kept snapping at me and Timmy.

Timmy kept crying and I felt guilty because it was the Barker that had caused all the trouble.

I tried cheering Timmy up by playing Duplo Lego with him. I tipped the box of bricks onto the floor of the sitting room and started making a wall.

'Mine!' Prince Timmy snatched a brick out of my hand.

'We have to share, Timmy,' I said and tried to prise the brick from his fingers.

'Mine!' he shrieked and bashed me on the head with the bright red brick.

'That hurt!' I shouted. He was only two but he was already practising fratricide.

'Wah!' Timmy screamed.

'Dan?' Mum rushed into the sitting room. 'What have you done now?'

I was about to say 'Nothing' when the doorbell rang. It was six o'clock exactly.

'That'll be Gordon,' I said. 'Can I let him in?'

'Yes, take him upstairs.' Mum picked up Timmy. My baby brother didn't clonk Mum on the head with the Lego brick, I noticed. He only thumped his zero brother. 'And just take one thing out of your cupboard at a time. It took me ages to tidy your room earlier.'

Gah! Mum had been upstairs messing with my stuff. Didn't she realise I'd set up my room like that for a reason? But I didn't bother mentioning it as she wasn't in the mood for an argument.

I let Gordon in and we went upstairs. The space under my loft bed was no longer a fortress full of my precious belongings. Mum had put everything away.

Gordon doesn't have a Random Mood Generator. He is in control of his emotions at all times. Even when he is angry and turns into the bulging-eyeball demon, he knows what he is doing. Today he was Gordon the Super-Efficient-Know-It-All. He sprayed my desk chair with disinfectant before I could stop him. He pulled something out of a bag and showed me a weird-looking binoculars case.

'Behold! The night-vision goggles,' he said.

'Great,' I said. 'Thanks so much, Gordon. Can I look at them?'

'There are some additional regulations that you must agree to first,' Gordon said.

'Anything.' My stomach was doing backflips like it does on Christmas morning. I really wanted to see the very expensive, brand-new goggles.

'The goggles must be kept in the case whenever you aren't wearing them,' Gordon said.

I nodded and shifted my chair a bit nearer.

'If you wear the goggles when the lights are on, you will go blind, and I am not responsible.'

I stood up to switch the lights off.

'Before you do that, sign here.' Gordon handed me a clipboard. 'They cost £697.95.'

'I'm borrowing them, not buying them,' I said.

'And if you break them?' Gordon said and he gave me a mind-drilling look. 'All breakages have to be paid for, don't you agree?'

At that moment, I remembered why Gordon was only my second best friend. Freddo would have lent me the goggles without any conditions, however expensive they were. But for once, Freddo didn't have the equipment I needed. I didn't have any choice. If I was going to catch the burglars I needed Gordon's super expensive night-vision goggles.

The piece of paper was full of small print. I sighed and signed it without bothering to read it.

Gordon put it in his briefcase.

If he had looked at it, he would have seen that Donald Duck had signed to say he would pay for breakages, not Daniel Kendal. I can be a rubbish friend too.

Gordon handed me a bottle of hand sanitizer, drew a ring round each of his eye sockets to remind me to disinfect myself before using the goggles, and left.

First, I squirted a quarter of the sanitizer down the sink in the bathroom so it looked like I had been an obedient friend. Then I explored the goggles.

They were like a pair of binoculars with a head harness. The binocular bit was on a hinge so I could flip them up, away from my eyes if I wanted to. There was a dimmer switch to adjust them to different light levels, and a zoom-in binocular function.

As soon as I put them on, I never wanted to take them off. They were the most awesome thing ever.

I turned off the lights and shut the door, but I could see every detail of my room in shades of 3D greeny-grey. It could have been magic not science. The burglars wouldn't be able to escape now. Daniel the Night-vision Detective was on their case.

I picked up my torch, pointed it away from me and switched it on. Woah! My torch beam transformed instantly into a real lightsaber. The green beam went on forever. I gripped the torch in both hands, assumed the Jedi fighting position and gave it a swipe.

Unfortunately my torch was a torch, not the most powerful weapon in the universe, and I was Daniel Kendal, not Luke Skywalker, so I wasn't going to be armed on the stake-out. But I didn't need to hurt the burglars. I needed to catch them and, thanks to Gordon, I was going to do just that.

# Night Vision in the Wild

I went to sleep in my almost-ninja outfit – black polo neck jumper, a black balaclava and black jeans. It would have been a total ninja outfit if I'd worn leggings but the only leggings in this house were in Jessie's bedroom and I wasn't going in there. Being a jeans-wearing almost-ninja was good enough.

I jumped out of bed the minute my alarm went off at midnight and made the final preparations for my stake-out. I hung Gordon's goggle case around my neck and pulled the night-vision goggles on over my head. I headed downstairs.

Dad is in charge of security in our house. He locks up every night but he leaves the key close to the front door so we can get out quick if there is a fire. When I got downstairs the key was on the hook as usual, but the top door lock was on the catch. I tried the handle and the door swung open. It wasn't locked at all. If I could open it then if anyone (like a burglar) touched the door from the outside, it would swing wide open.

Dad knew that burglars were targeting our neighbourhood but he hadn't even locked the door! What was wrong with him? Had he gone totally mental? Was he so stressed by everything that was going on that he had forgotten even the most basic security measures?

I checked I had my own keys on me, flipped the catch on the top lock down and pulled the front door closed behind me. I used my big key to double lock the door from the outside. No one was going through that door while I was away snooping around the street. I was taking security a lot more seriously than Dad.

The night-vision goggles turned Beechwood Road into a giant hologram. Outside was brighter than inside the house because of the street lights, so I turned down the goggles' dimmer switch so the brightness didn't hurt my eyes. I crept down the path like a true ninja and stepped out onto the pavement. The houses were mainly dark except

for slits of green light shining through the curtains where someone was watching late-night TV. Traffic hummed along the main road but it sounded miles away. The only movement was at the end of the road. A torch beam flitted backwards and forwards along the pavement and it was heading this way.

I wasn't sure if it was someone walking their dog or whether it was the burglars. I squeezed myself in between the wheelie bins by the side of our front path and listened as the footsteps got nearer and nearer. I couldn't hear the pitter-patter of dog paws, so it wasn't a dog walker. I froze. It must be a burglar!

I wished Freddo had come on this stake-out with me. On TV, detectives always have a partner. I was about to come face to face with a real-life burglar and I was on my own.

The footsteps passed in front of my house and the torch beam came into sight. Even though it wasn't pointing at me, the light was so bright it made my eyes sting. I dimmed my goggles a bit more. The torch-wielding burglar walked on a little further, then crossed the road.

'Pssst! Are you there?' a voice hissed.

Rats! He was calling for his accomplice – or accomplices. There might be a gang of them! I pressed myself further into the gap between the bins.

The burglar walked past all the houses flashing

his torch through the front gardens towards the front doors. I figured he was checking which houses were occupied and which were dark. But he was a pretty stupid burglar bringing a torch with him. If anyone looked out of their window, they would see him even without night-vision goggles.

I heard a strange noise, like a car backfiring, and the burglar crossed the road, waving his torch in the air.

The beam of light was on our house now. He was shining his light right at my bedroom window. He was about to break in!

I needed to phone the police but I couldn't because my hands were shaking so much. The burglar lowered his light and started walking up our path. His footsteps got louder the closer he got to me. So did my thumping heartbeat. The criminal was less than a metre away when he suddenly flicked his light between the wheelie bins right into my face, blinding me completely.

'Gotcha!' he said.

# 11 Caught in the Act

Pins, needles, swords, arrows, knives. In my eyes. All at once.

I flipped the night-vision goggles up and tried to clutch hold of my burning eyeballs. The pain! The pain! Exploding dynamite had been planted in my head.

'Dan? You all right, mate?' The burglar's voice sounded familiar. 'Dan?' A cheese-and-onion-smelling person knelt in front of me. 'I've been looking for you.'

'Freddo?' I looked up but all I could see was brightness and darkness all at the same time.

'Yeah, it's me,' Freddo said. 'Who did you think it was?'

'A burglar,' I said. 'Switch that flipping torch off, will you? You've blinded me. I don't think I'll ever see again.'

Some of the light went out and Freddo pulled me to my feet. I flipped my night-vision goggles down but it didn't help. My brain was seeing stars that weren't there.

'Can I help you with that?' Freddo slipped the goggles off my head and slung the case over his shoulder.

'Be careful,' I said. 'I've signed something to say I won't drop them.'

'I'm not going to drop them, I'm going to wear them!' Freddo's voice had that gleeful tone to it – the one he uses when he discovers a bag of crisps in the bottom of his school bag that he had forgotten about.

Oh crud! Gordon would go mad if he knew what Freddo was doing, but there was nothing I could do about it. I was too blind to stop him.

'Wow!' Freddo said. 'This is awesome! I am so going to put these on my Christmas list.' He wandered away from me oohing and ahhing at the way the world looked through Gordon's über-gadget but suddenly his voice changed. 'Oh! Flipping dog poo!' he muttered.

'What dog poo?' I said.

'On the pavement,' Freddo said. 'It still stinks.'

It smelt worse than ever, in fact. I think it's true that if you lose one of your five senses, the other four kick in stronger. I couldn't see Freddo, but I could smell the bottom of his trainers. I stumbled after him because I didn't want to be left alone while I was blind. Freddo stinks most of the time but he was the best friend I had.

'Can I have the goggles back now?' I said when I bumped into him. 'I want to go home.'

'Wait!' Freddo grabbed my arm and pulled me to the pavement by Mr Elson's hedge. His elbow and the goggles poked me in the ribs but I didn't dare move.

'What is it? Tell me. I can't see a thing.'

'There's someone by your front door. Trying to get in. Two people.' He gripped my arm really tightly. 'They are definitely trying to break in.'

Thank goodness I locked the door. If it had been down to Dad and his rubbish security, those thieves would be inside ransacking my house right now while my family were asleep in bed.

'They're trying the door again,' Freddo said. 'It's not opening.'

'Call the police.' I fumbled with my phone. I could just make out the screen lighting up.

'Whoa! That's bright,' Freddo said, pushing my hand away.

'Flick your goggles up and phone the flipping police before the burglars get away!'

'Hang on a minute,' Freddo said. 'They're kissing!'

I squinted towards my house. I could just make out a shape standing on the path. A person. No, two people close together.

'Give me those goggles.' I tried to take them off Freddo's head but I couldn't see clearly enough to release the straps. 'There's a binocular function. You can zoom in on them. Get a close look so you can identify them in a police line-up.'

Freddo fiddled with a switch.

'Eugh! Yuk! They're snogging now!'

Snogging burglars?!

'Freddo, call the police, PLEASE,' I said.

'I can't do that, mate.' Freddo slumped onto the ground next to me.

'Why not?' I said, stabbing randomly at my phone.

Freddo put his hand over mine and took my phone away.

'Because one of those burglars is Jessie.'

That was the moment I made an amazing scientific discovery: absolute terror is the perfect cure for temporary blindness.

Suddenly I could see again and what I could see was Jessie and Dazzer with their arms around each other and their mouths stuck together like a couple of vacuum cleaners.

Totally disgusting – yes, but terrifying also.

Here's the thing:

- I was outside in the middle of the night, illegally looking for burglars.
- The only people I had found were Jessie and Dazzer, snogging.
- I couldn't get back into the house because the snoggers were blocking my way.
- Jessie couldn't get back into the house because I had locked the door thinking that Dad had left it undone by mistake, when in fact Jessie had left it like that on purpose so she could sneak back in without making a sound.

When Jessie realised what I had done, she would definitely give fratricide a go and I'd be zilch, nada, zero forever because I would be dead.

I leant against Mr Elson's hedge in a haze of stinking dog poo from Freddo's shoe and waited for the inevitable.

'She won't forgive me for this one. You know that gravestone everyone was talking about in class?' I said to Freddo. 'Promise me you'll have an inscription carved.'

'Give me your keys.' Freddo held out his hand. 'Let me show you how it's done.' He swapped the night-vision goggles for my keys and walked towards my house.

I put the goggles on and peered over Mr Elson's

gate, bracing myself for the sight of Freddo's blood in night vision.

Freddo sauntered up our path. 'Morning, Jessie. Daz,' he said as he skirted past the snogging couple.

They sprang apart as if someone had stabbed them with an electric cattle prod.

Freddo unlocked the front door, opened it wide and took a theatrical bow.

'See you later.' He smiled his hypnotising smile and walked away.

Jessie looked at Daz. Daz looked at Jessie. They had a quick kiss goodbye and Jessie dashed into the house, shutting the door behind her.

'Simples!' Freddo said when he came back to me.

'Thanks, mate,' I spluttered and for the first time ever I gave my best friend a hug.

'Mind if I go home?' Freddo said. 'I'm bored of looking for burglars tonight.'

'Me too,' I said. All I wanted was my bed and sleep. Narrowly avoiding certain death was exhausting.

'See you later!' Freddo shoved my keys and the night-vision goggles case in my hand. 'Be careful with that, it's got dog poo on it.'

'What?!'

But Freddo didn't say anything else.

I watched as my very best friend walked away, shining his torch before him so he could see what he was stepping on.

I was still in a state of shock when I let myself back into the house dangling a totally contaminated night-vision goggles case. It didn't matter how much sanitizer I used, Gordon would know that his case had been in contact with stinky dog poo. I crept upstairs and was about to go to my room, when someone grabbed my shoulder.

I could tell Jessie's random mood by her wide-eyed glare:

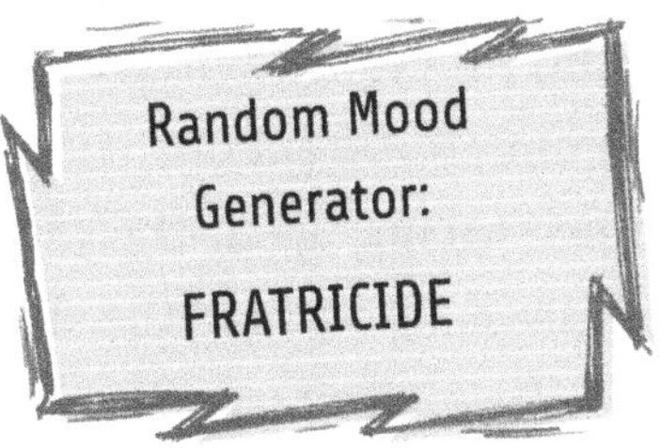


I decided to handle this Freddo-style.

'Shh!' I put my finger to my lips. 'You'll wake the baby.' I removed her hand from my shoulder and went into my room. I shut the door behind me and took a series of very deep breaths.

# The Case of the Missing Xbox

Somehow I'd survived being murdered by Jessie, but in the morning I had to tell Gordon what had happened to the precious night-vision goggles case, and it wasn't going to be pretty.

I had trouble waking up in the morning. I'm not used to prowling around half the night, and to be honest I was a little worried what Jessie would do to me in daylight.

Mum, Dad, Timmy and Jessie were all munching on their toast when I went down to the kitchen.

'Have you had your breakfast?' Mum said.

'No, I overslept.' I slumped in my chair. My seat is opposite Jessie's but I didn't dare look up in case

I caught her eye.

'Is that your new image?' Dad looked me up and down. 'You know, Goth? Black clothes. Black eye make-up.'

Jessie snorted.

'I'm not wearing make-up,' I said.

'What's that black round your eyes then?' Dad said.

I guessed it was dark shadows under my eyes from no sleep and of course I was dressed in black because I had fallen asleep wearing my almost-ninja outfit.

Dad shoved a piece of bread in the toaster and stared out of the window while it cooked.

'Oh no! It's the police again!' he said, shaking his head.

'Oh no!' Mum said. 'Where are they going this time?'

'Number twenty-two, Mrs Brown's. There must have been another burglary.'

How was that even possible? Two people from this family were outside for most of the night. We'd have spotted the burglars. Unless . . .

I looked at Jessie. Could she and Dazzer be the burglars?

She looked at me and narrowed her eyes in a 'Don't say a word' sort of way.

Jessie and Dazzer had been outside for ages before Freddo and I saw them. They could have broken into Mrs Brown's before they snogged their faces off on our front path. That meant they had the opportunity. But did they have the means or the motive?

Jessie never did anything like this when she was only in love with One Dimension. No wonder Mum and Dad didn't like her hanging out with Dazzer all the time.

The doorbell rang and Dad went to answer it. It was Mr Elson. They chatted for a little while, but however hard I tried I couldn't hear what they were saying as I munched on my cereal.

'Yeah, it was Mrs Brown who was burgled last night,' Dad said when he came back in. 'But they only took Victor's Xbox.'

Jessie has always wanted an Xbox! That means she had a motive for breaking into Mrs Brown's house. But did she have the means? She did have a load of nail files which would be perfect for forcing locks . . .

Means, motive and opportunity. The three words sideswiped me so hard I nearly fell off my seat. Jessie

and Dazzer were the burglars! I tried to glare at her, to tell her I knew she was guilty, but she wouldn't look me in the eye.

'Victor's at university, isn't he?' Mum said.

'Yes, but apparently he's very attached to his Xbox and left her with all sorts of instructions not to touch it because he was at a very important stage in his game when term started.'

'That's why we're not getting an Xbox,' Mum said.

Jessie gave me a particularly hard kick under the table.

'Mr Elson says that someone must have been hanging around his front garden last night because someone has trampled in his flower beds and smeared footprints all over the path and pavement. And needless to say it wasn't just mud.' Dad tutted before he bit into his piece of toast.

Dog poo! A rock of doom smashed into my stomach. It wasn't just Mr Elson's path that was dirty. Gordon's case was also contaminated and he was going to go ballistic when he found out.

'Mrs Brown is also upset because her cat's gone missing,' Dad said. 'The burglar must have let it out when he was ransacking the house. She's devastated. There's a meeting at the community centre tonight to discuss the burglaries.'

'You go, but I've got Zumba,' Mum said. 'Jessie, you can babysit as you're still grounded.'

Jessie scowled but didn't say anything.

'I don't need a babysitter,' I said. What I really needed was a bodyguard. Either Jessie or Gordon was going to kill me very soon.

'You can come with me to the meeting,' Dad said to me. 'I think we all need to know what's going on around here.'

# Lie Detection Made Easy

I agreed to go to the meeting with Dad mainly because it meant I would be out of the house when Gordon came round waving a contract in the air signed by Donald Duck and demanding a new pair of night-vision goggles in a brand-new case. I didn't need to hear what the police were doing to find out the identity of the burglars. I already knew who they were.

Jessie and Dazzer.

They had been doing a lot of hanging out at McDonald's and the bowling alley with all their mates recently and there was no way Jessie could be going out to those places on one pound a week pocket money. (Jessie and I get the same pocket money and we've never had a pay rise.) They must have been selling the stuff they nicked to pay for all those burgers and fries. That is a strong motive to commit burglary.

It was pretty mean of them to steal Victor's Xbox when he was in the middle of a level. He used to be our babysitter. He's our friend and even though Jessie had always wanted an Xbox, she couldn't have it at home as Mum would go mad. So where was the stolen Xbox now?

I seriously thought about telling Mum and Dad what I knew about the burglaries the next morning.

TELL MUM AND DAD THAT JESSIE IS THE BURGLAR

| PROS | CONS |
| --- | --- |
| ? | Jessie would kill me. |
| | They wouldn't believe me because I am the zero child. |
| | There'd be a terrible row, which would make Timmy cry. |
| | I don't want to be a snitch. |

I didn't have much choice. I had to keep quiet.

'Time for school, Dan,' Mum yelled up the stairs.

I slammed my notebook shut and prepared myself for the next problem: Gordon the neat-freak Geek and the dog-poo goggle case.

Outside, the street was full of nosy neighbours I didn't recognise looking at the police car.

A tall man wearing a thick overcoat blocked the pavement by our gate. He had his arm round a short woman wearing too much jewellery. I guess she thought that wearing her bling was safer than leaving it at home. She had a white furry scarf wrapped up in her arms. It probably had even more valuables hidden inside.

'Daniel,' Mr Elson called out to me as I reached our gate. 'Will you tell me if you see anyone not cleaning up after their dog?'

I nodded, and then pulled up my hoodie and tried to be anonymous in case he started asking awkward questions about what I was doing last night. But I think he was more concerned about cleaning his path.

'I'm absolutely fed up with stinking mess

everywhere.' Mr Elson swooshed a bucket of steaming water over his front path. 'I'm offering a reward to anyone who catches them.'

The woman hugged her furry scarf closer to her. She grabbed the man's arm and crossed the road to join the crowd hanging around outside Mrs Brown's house.

I gave Mr Elson a mental thumbs up for washing away all the evidence that Freddo and I had been in his front garden and sprinted down the road towards school.

Gordon's desk was still empty when I walked into the classroom but Freddo was already there waiting for the crisps I'd promised him for helping me record Lucy's barking.

'What a total nightmare I've had this morning!' I said as I handed over two packets of cheese and onion and one ready salted. 'You managed to spread dog poo all over Mr Elson's front garden as well as on Gordon's goggle case.'

'Yeah?' Freddo opened his first crisp packet of the day and tipped the whole contents into his mouth. His cheeks bulged and bits of crisp splattered out as he tried to chew.

'Mr Elson cleaned up his garden and our footprints so I think we've got away with that, but how am I going to clean Gordon's case?'

Freddo shrugged. 'Buy him a new one.'

Buying something was Freddo's answer to everything. It was all right for him, he got ten pounds weekly pocket money. I didn't want to have to turn to crime like Jessie.

'Where am I going to get that sort of money from?' I said, but even as the words came out of my mouth something else sparked in my head. Mr Elson had said he would offer a reward to whoever caught the doggie poopers.

How much of a reward?

Fifty pounds?

One hundred pounds?

Enough to buy a brand-new night-vision goggles case?

'Where do you think I'd buy a case like that anyway?' I said.

Freddo nudged me to shut up as Gordon walked into the classroom. He wore a navy blazer with brass buttons down the front. He ignored us as usual and unpacked his briefcase. He adjusted the exact position of his laptop, pencil case and notebook using his ruler and set squares.

'Nice blazer, Gordon,' I said, hoping to put him in a good mood before he asked any awkward questions.

'Good morning.' He nudged his pencil case into perfect alignment and then turned to speak to me. 'Was the stake-out successful?'

'Not exactly,' I said.

'Where are my night-vision goggles?' Gordon said.

'Safely at home,' I blurted out. 'I thought Mr Pitdown would confiscate them if I brought them to school.'

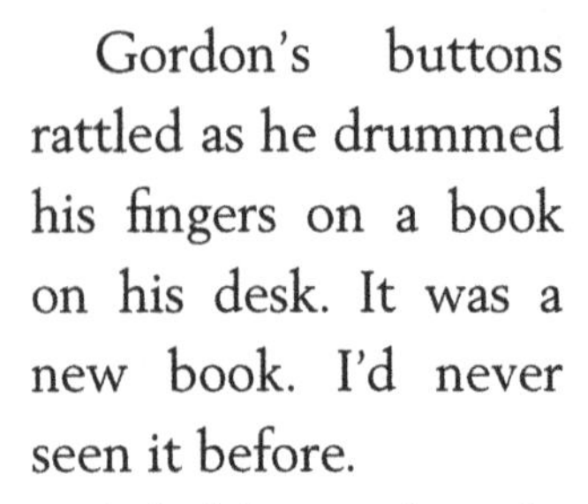

Gordon's buttons rattled as he drummed his fingers on a book on his desk. It was a new book. I'd never seen it before.

I held my breath, waiting for the explosion. Gordon placed his hand flat on the book and stood motionless until his buttons were still, then he nodded and sat down at his seat.

Phew! That was a narrow escape.

'Gordon, mate?' Freddo said.

I gave Freddo a sharp kick. Using the word 'mate' was not part of my plan to keep Gordon happy.

'I mean, Gordon, sir,' Freddo said. 'Sir Gordon, can I ask you a question?'

Gordon didn't answer at first but I think that being called Sir Gordon made him feel like the boss on *The Apprentice* so he nodded and said, 'You may proceed.'

'Where did you get those goggles from?' Freddo said.

'I bought them from spymastergeneralstores.com,' Gordon said.

'Do they sell the case separately?' Freddo said.

'I believe so.' Gordon frowned a little and his fingers edged towards his lie detection book.

'There you go, mate.' Freddo turned to me. 'Spymasterwhatsit.com.'

Freddo doesn't know when to keep his cheese-and-onion mouth shut.

Gordon stood up, turned round and took a step towards me. His eyes fixed on me and I'm sure I could hear the high-pitched whine of a drill starting up.

'Why do you want to buy a new night-vision goggles case?' As Gordon's eyes started drilling into my brain, his lips jammed shut so tightly I don't know how he was able to speak.

'My fault,' Freddo said. 'I accidentally dropped it in some dog poo last night.'

The temperature in the classroom dropped ten degrees. Even Rooners and the football gang started rubbing their arms and stamping their feet to keep warm and they were on the other side of the room.

Gordon rose out of his seat and came towards me. His eyeballs pulsed in their sockets but his black pupils were fixed firmly on the space between my eyes. I think he was assessing the best spot to kill me outright.

'Freddo touched my case. Freddo touched my night-vision goggles.' They weren't questions. They were statements. Gordon knew the truth.

'I can explain,' I said. 'It was an accident. Freddo didn't mean to —'

But Gordon wasn't listening. He picked up *Lie Detection for Beginners* in both hands. He raised his hands above his head and prepared to knock my head off my shoulders.

At that moment I made up a new word.

Friendicide.

And I was about to become the first victim.

# 14 What Happened Next

Jessie is not the only person who thinks I am a zilch, nada, zero. Mr Pitdown agrees with her, but luckily for me Mr Pitdown has certain responsibilities to the kids in his class because he is a teacher.

At precisely the moment Gordon began bringing *Lie Detection for Beginners* towards my head, Mr Pitdown walked into the room.

'Gordon Franks!' he yelled.

No one had ever spoken to Gordon like that before. His body quivered. His eyes jiggled in their sockets. His hands twitched. *Lie Detection for Beginners* (hardback) fell and smacked Gordon on the top of his own head.

The Geek staggered against a desk, holding his head in his hands.

'I'm sorry,' I said. 'I'm so sorry.' I picked up Gordon's book and tried to return it to him.

'I don't need that any more!' Gordon shoved it back at me. 'I know who has been lying around here.'

'I didn't lie! I didn't ask Freddo to come with me last night. He just showed up.'

Gordon glared at me through half-closed eyes. I could feel him drilling into my brain again, trying to find out the truth. He didn't need his book – he clearly already knew every lie-detecting technique in it.

'I'll buy you a new case,' I said, but my voice sounded whiny and pathetic. 'Your goggles are safe in a box at home. I promise you.'

CLAP. CLAP. CLAPPITY. CLAP.

Mr Pitdown tried to get everyone's attention.

I saw a flicker of distraction in Gordon's eyes but he didn't relax.

'You are telling the truth,' he said. 'But what if

you are burgled? My goggles might be stolen.'

'No chance.' Freddo pushed in front of me, breaking Gordon's line of sight. 'Your goggles are safer at Dan's than round at yours, Gordon. We know who the burglars are. It's Jessie and her boyfriend. And they are never going to burgle their own house.'

Gordon's eyebrows shot up into his hair and he gripped the edge of my desk so that he didn't fall over in amazement.

'Gordon! What has got into you today?' Mr Pitdown rapped his knuckles on Gordon's desk.

Gordon dropped his eyebrows and returned to his desk. He took his set square out and checked that Mr Pitdown hadn't moved his pencil case. As soon as Mr Pitdown's back was turned, Gordon turned round and whispered, 'Jessie? Really?'

'Really!' Freddo and I whispered back.

I felt very uncomfortable telling Gordon that my sister was a thief. No one wants to have a criminal in their own family and I was worried that Gordon wouldn't want to be my friend any more, but at least it kept his mind off the dog-poo-covered goggles case.

We were in our usual playground spot under the fire escape when we told Gordon all about it.

'Will she get a custodial sentence?' Gordon had to shout because he wouldn't get close to Freddo while he had an open packet of crisps in his hand.

'What's a custardy sentence?' I said.

'Will she go to prison?' Gordon clarified.

A rock of doom the size of Mars hit me in the stomach. Jessie in prison? I hadn't thought of that. She'd hate it. She had tap-dancing exams coming up, she'd be separated from Dazzer and they probably wouldn't let her have all her One Dimension posters. She'd never survive. Jessie can be very annoying sometimes but she is still my sister and our house would be very quiet without her.

'Nah,' Freddo said. 'Not for a first offence. Not unless she used violence.'

'She hit me with her hair straighteners once,' I said.

'That doesn't count,' Freddo said.

'I think you should tell your parents,' Gordon said.

'No way!' I said. 'Do you want a nuclear explosion to wipe out the whole town?'

Gordon looked over his glasses at me with his bored-professor look. He didn't like it when I ignored his suggestions. He opened his laptop and started typing.

'I've got a plan,' I said. 'But it's a rubbish one. There's a meeting tonight at the community centre. I'm going with Dad. The police are going to tell everyone what's going on,' I said.

'So?' Freddo shrugged.

'Do you think it would be possible to lay some false clues to confuse the police?' I looked over at Gordon. He didn't look up, but his ears twitched a little so I knew he was listening. 'Maybe the police would start looking somewhere else while I persuade Jessie to give up her life of crime.'

'Could work,' Freddo said. 'Will Jessie listen to you?'

'No,' I said. 'But she'll listen to you.'

'You reckon?' Freddo balled his crisp packet and threw it at my head.

'Please, Freddo,' I said. 'She hates me.'

He looked at me for a moment, and then nodded. 'You go to your meeting. I'll see what I can do about Jessie.'

# The Problem With Meetings

The community hall was packed when Dad and I got to the meeting. Everyone wanted to know how the police were going to catch the burglars. I wanted to know how to stop them catching the burglars.

In amongst the audience I spotted Mr Elson (from next door) and Carol Duffy (who was burgled the other day).

'Coo-ee!' Carol called across to Dad and patted the empty seat next to her. Dad did a bit of sign language to explain that I was with him and we found two seats next to each other at the back. Mum would have been proud of him. She really didn't like Dad being friends with Miss Duffy. Ever since Dad offered to help Miss Duffy trim the front hedge but ended up staying all afternoon to mow her lawn, dig her flower beds and help her drink two bottles of wine, while our own garden still looked like a jungle. Mum was furious.

Mrs Bling, the lady who had been at our gate in the morning with the fur scarf in her arms, was sitting in the front row.

On the little stage, a row of tired-looking people sat behind a table looking at the audience. One was wearing a police uniform with all sorts of shiny bits stuck to it. He stood up and called the meeting to attention. Everyone ignored him and carried on talking. He asked for quiet again, but it was ages before everyone settled down. He obviously hadn't learnt *Clap. Clap. Clappity. Clap* at police school. In the end he had to smack his water bottle on the table ten times before there was silence in the room.

The silver-foiled police officer introduced himself as Chief Super-Something-or-other. He droned on about all sorts of things that I didn't understand and then he introduced a plain-clothes police officer and sat down. Inspector Locke was different. His suit was a bit shabby and his shirt had never been

ironed, but he looked alert, so I paid attention. He clicked something and a diagram of our street appeared on the screen above his head. The map was almost identical to Gordon's one but it had a massive X through Mrs Brown's house. Inspector Locke didn't know how to iron his clothes but he seemed suspiciously like a good detective.

The audience fell totally silent and so did I. Jessie and Dazzer were going to be caught for sure.

'We don't have much to go on,' Inspector Locke

said. 'There were no fingerprints or DNA evidence at the crime scenes. But from the CCTV set up by Mrs Gonzales, we have put together some e-fit pictures.'

CCTV!

E-fit pictures!

Panic bubbled up inside me. Someone in this room was going to recognise Jessie. It would probably be Dad. He'd make a total scene. He'd take Jessie down to the police station and confess everything. That's what he did to me when I accidentally brought Spike Munroe's complete Pokémon card collection home with me in Year Three. Actually he didn't take me to the police, he took me to the playground supervisor at school, which was bad enough and I hadn't even broken the law.

Jessie and Dazzer were going to jail!

'There are three suspects,' Inspector Locke continued.

STOP!

REWIND!

How many suspects? Three? Jessie and Dazzer but who was the third?

'Take a good look at these pictures.' Inspector

Locke handed a stack of leaflets to someone in the front row and asked everyone to pass them round. 'Show them to the rest of your family. Someone must know them.' The room buzzed with unhappy neighbours as more and more people got a leaflet. Everyone hated those faces in front of them. Everyone wanted the police to arrest them.

Poor Jessie. She was only four years older than me. She probably didn't realise how serious this was. She'd been led on by Dazzer and Suspect Number Three. Things had got out of hand. She'd got in too deep and now it was too late to save her. She was bound to be arrested by the end of the evening.

'Can we go home now?' I said to Dad. I needed to get him out of that room without seeing the picture of his eldest child with the words *Wanted Dead or Alive* printed across her face. He wasn't going to take it very well. And Mum? Well, she'd probably have to go to a special hospital for parents who can't cope with their naughty children. I stood up to go, hoping he'd follow me.

'Not until I've got one of those leaflets,' Dad said. 'We need to show it to Jessie and Mum, and all your friends. Freddo might recognise them. Or Dazzer.'

Dad didn't know how right he was. 'I hadn't realised someone in the street had CCTV,' I said.

'That new lady over the road rigged something up to spy on the back alley. You must have seen her,' Dad said. 'She carries that stupid mutt everywhere.'

'You mean the short lady in the front row with lots of jewellery?'

'Yeah,' Dad said.

Mrs Bling! A dog-poo-shaped light bulb suddenly lit up in my head.

'She says her dog kept barking so she knew people were prowling around,' Dad said.

'I don't think that is the only thing her dog keeps doing,' I said, but Dad wasn't listening.

It wasn't a coincidence that a new dog moved into the street at the same time as dog poo became a problem. Mr and Mrs

Bling were very quick to move away when Mr Elson started moaning about dog poo the other morning and I suspected that it wasn't a fur scarf bundled up in Mrs Bling's arms. It was a werepoodle with a very active digestive tract. And Mrs Bling probably didn't want to put her bling anywhere near dog poo, not even to scoop the poop. I needed to speak to Mr Elson and claim my reward.

The pile of leaflets was getting closer, but it was getting smaller as well. Maybe there wouldn't be enough leaflets to reach the back row and Dad would never know what Jessie had been up to . . .

'Are there any more questions?' asked Inspector Locke.

'I want to raise the issue of dog mess on the pavements,' Mr Elson said.

Don't mention the reward! I repeated over and over in my head in case Mr Elson was telepathic. I needed that money to replace Gordon's case.

'Can we confine questions to the subject of burglaries?' Inspector Locke said. But the remaining audience were no longer interested in burglaries.

'It's disgusting.'

'It's foul.'

'It's unhygienic.'

The telepathy thing must have worked because Mr Elson didn't mention the reward.

'My cat Henry has gone missing,' Mrs Brown said in a quivery voice. 'I need him back. I'm all alone now Victor has gone to university.'

But no one was listening – they were all too busy swapping 'dog poo on my shoe' stories. Inspector Locke tried to get them back on topic, but it was too late. The meeting was over.

'I haven't got a leaflet,' Dad said as he tried to push his way to the front of the hall.

'Let's go home.' I tugged on his jumper but he completely ignored me.

'There's one!' Dad suddenly lunged forward and picked up a piece of paper from the floor.

I couldn't breathe. I couldn't speak. I couldn't move. I wanted to protect Jessie, but it was impossible. She'd done the crime. She was going to have to do the time. There was nothing I could do to help her now.

'What a bunch of weirdos!' Dad said as he studied the poster. 'Do you recognise any of them?'

HAVE
YOU
SEEN
THESE
SUSPECTS?

# The Three Suspects

I remember being in the community hall with a horrid, sick feeling in my stomach and I remember being at home with an even worse feeling in my whole body. Something must have happened in-between but I can't remember. All I could think about was the picture of me and my two best friends on the Wanted poster.

We were detectives, not burglars! Jessie and Dazzer were the real burglars. I'd seen them outside at night, but yet again I was going to get the blame for everything when I was totally innocent.

Mum was back from Zumba and Dad called Jessie out of her teen lair. He sat everyone down at the table and told them all about the meeting.

Jessie's Random Mood Generator was set on BORED. She didn't look at Dad, she didn't listen to what he was saying. She turned her chair halfway from the table and filed her nails. She didn't look like someone worried that the police might be onto her.

And then I realised why.

She didn't use a metal nail file, she used emery boards. Cardboard covered in sandpaper. She wouldn't be able to force a lock with them. Maybe she didn't have the means to be a burglar after all.

I didn't have the means either, but my face was now plastered all over the neighbourhood. I could never leave the house again.

Mum stared at the Wanted poster, shaking her head and muttering phrases like, 'What is the world coming to?' and 'Their poor parents, I don't expect they meant to bring criminals into this world.'

I think my parents have got something seriously wrong with their eyesight. Neither of them recognised the three suspects even though one of them was sitting at the table opposite them.

'If any of you see these guys,' Mum said, 'you are

not to go up to them. They look like total hard nuts.'

Jessie snatched the photo out of her hand. She scowled, looked up at me, then looked down at the photo again. She narrowed her eyes and was about to say something, but I got in first.

'Seen Dazzer recently?'

Jessie snapped her mouth shut, threw the leaflet on the table and left the room with a slam.

What a nightmare! I needed to get hold of Freddo urgently. If he tried to persuade Jessie to give up her supposed life of crime, she'd go mental. Then she'd point out to Mum and Dad that the faces on the Wanted poster looked very much like Freddo, Gordon and me. Mum and Dad would take us to the police station and we would be in jail.

I had never been in such serious trouble. My stomach was doing backflips and twisters all over the place. It was like having a nuclear-powered roller coaster right inside me.

Timmy picked up the leaflet and smiled.

'Dan, Dan,' he said and pointed to the picture of the almost-ninja.

Luckily Mum and Dad were too busy discussing whether an extra bolt was needed on the front door to take any notice of him.

'Ed-doh.' He pointed to the picture of a packet of crisps. 'Geek-geek.' He pointed to Gordon the crime scene investigator.

Even though my guts were wrenching this way and that I felt a small seed of happiness. Someone loved me enough to recognise me.

'Thanks, Timmy,' I said and held out my hand for the leaflet.

'Dan, Dan,' Timmy said and then scrunched the paper into a ball and threw it on the floor.

'Thanks, Timmy. NOT!' Even my baby brother, Prince Timmy, thought I was a zilch, nada, zero. The small speck of happiness shrivelled to nothing and my guts yanked themselves into a knot.

If a two year old recognised me and my friends, it wouldn't be long before someone else did, whether Jessie said anything or not. I had to do something drastic right away.

My head whirled with loads of stupid ideas like

running away to join the circus or persuading my two best friends to change their appearance by shaving their heads and having their noses pierced, but somehow I didn't think Gordon would go for it.

I could lay a trail of false clues to confuse the police, but knowing my luck I'd do it wrong and the trail would lead them straight back to me.

In the end I decided there was only one course of action: we needed to catch the real burglars before the police realised who the three faces belonged to and arrested the wrong people. Us!

That was the only way to avoid arrest, or Freddo, Gordon and I would be sharing jail time very soon. And while I like my two friends, I didn't think being locked up together in a prison cell was a good idea.

I picked the leaflet up, smoothed it out and put it in my school bag. I didn't know how we were going to catch the real crooks, but we needed to do it fast.

Mr Pitdown was in one of his mean moods so he let us out late for break. Break time is only twenty minutes, which isn't long enough for The Geek to get his computer fix, Freddo to get his crisp fix AND for me to brief them about the latest unfortunate development so I had to speak very quickly when we finally got together at our usual spot by the fire escape.

'Before I start, Freddo have you spoken to Jessie yet?'

Freddo looked at me blankly over his packet of crisps. 'About what?'

'I'll take that as a "no" then. Good. Don't speak to her about giving up her life of crime because there have been certain developments.' I took a deep breath. 'Do you want the good news or the bad news?' I asked the team.

'Good,' Freddo said.

'Bad,' Gordon said, but he didn't look up.

I think that sums up the difference between my two best friends.

'Good news is the police have released e-fit photos of three suspects and Jessie isn't one of them,' I said. 'The bad news is – these are the pictures.' I handed the leaflet to Freddo.

Freddo coughed. His face turned tomato-ish and he grabbed his throat.

I thumped him hard on the back. Gordon took a few steps backwards, out of range.

'Do you need water?' I said to Freddo.

He shook his head and shoved more crisps down his throat, then he stuck the packet in his mouth and chewed on that. After a few minutes, he stopped choking and pulled the crunched bag out of his mouth. He was able to breathe again.

'When you said "bad news", I didn't think you meant that bad,' he said.

'What are we going to do?'

'Time for reinforcements.' Freddo fumbled in his bag and pulled out a packet of extra-strong chilli crisps.

'Gordon, we've got a problem,' I called across to our friend, who had moved even further away when the extra-strong chilli came out. 'We need you. This time the bad news is connected to us.' I propped the leaflet on top of his typing hands, in front of his laptop screen so he had to look at it.

Gordon looked up at the sky and carried on typing for a minute or two, then he pressed Enter with a flourish. He adjusted his glasses, detached his fingers from his keyboard and took the leaflet in both hands. Then he did something I'd never seen before.

His eyeballs shrank back into his head, his lips disappeared and his hands began shaking like an out of control washing machine. He made a weird sound in his throat (he might have been choking on his lips), his body went limp and he slumped to the ground.

Gordon, my geeky friend, lay on the tarmac. He looked so small and helpless. His glasses were crooked and his sunken eyes were still open but they were pretty lifeless as they stared out at me. I crouched down to check he was still breathing.

'Stand back!' Freddo rolled up his sleeves. 'I've got a first aid badge.'

'No, you haven't,' I said.

'Well, I would have done if I hadn't been thrown out of cub scouts.'

Freddo had only been to cubs once. So had I. We'd been together but quickly realised it wasn't for us.

'You can't touch him!' I said as Freddo's extra-stong-chilli-flavoured fingers went towards Gordon's neck. 'The shock will kill him.'

'We have to get the laptop string away from his neck,' Freddo said. 'It's strangling him.'

'I'll do it,' I said. 'You call a teacher.' But Freddo didn't move.

I gently eased the laptop string over Gordon's head and tried to move the laptop away.

'Mine!' Gordon croaked and snatched the laptop back.

'I was trying to help you,' I said.

'You were trying to rob me!' He sat up and straightened his glasses.

'No, I'm not,' I said.

'The police think you are a burglar.' He prodded

the picture of me. 'It's you and your sister.'

'Jessie isn't the burglar. That was a mistake,' I said. 'The police think we are the burglars.' I pointed to the three of us. 'There was a CCTV camera down the back alley by the werepoodle.'

Gordon squealed and clutched hold of his head.

'I knew something had happened to my brain,' he moaned. Gordon has this weird idea that video cameras can suck out your brainpower. 'I have been exposed to a camera. I have lost ten billion brain cells. AND IT IS ALL YOUR FAULT!'

'I'm sorry, Gordon, I didn't know about the camera,' I said.

Gordon rolled on the pavement, cradling his head in his arms.

'It's not the camera, we should be worried about, it's the photos,' Freddo said. 'What are we going to do now?'

# 17 Our Own CCTV

It took us a while to persuade Gordon that being caught on CCTV wasn't the end of the world. He was still alive, even though he was a weird shade of grey, but that might have been a reflection off the tarmac.

Once he was upright again, we started making our plan.

'I suggest we use the same tactics that made us prime suspects,' I said. 'We need to set up our own CCTV cameras.'

Gordon whimpered.

'My dad's got loads,' Freddo said.

'Gordon's brain is obviously going to need some protection,' I said but before I could continue,

Gordon interrupted.

'What about the rest of me?' he stuttered. He still hadn't fully recovered from the shock of seeing his geeky face looking out of that Wanted poster.

Freddo groaned and rolled his eyes.

'Just to be on the safe side, I think we should protect his whole body,' I said quickly before Gordon collapsed again. 'Does your dad have any geek-sized wetsuits, Freddo? Extra thick ones with a built in balaclava for snorkelling in the Arctic and protecting brainpower?'

'I'll see what I can do,' Freddo said.

'There is one fault with your plan, Mr Kendal,' Gordon said. 'The burglars might not come to your home to commit their crime. They might burgle someone else.'

I was surprised that Gordon had the energy to call me Mr Kendal, but he did have a point.

'If we leave a load of computer and TV packaging outside your house,' Freddo said, 'they'll think you've got something worth stealing.'

'Great idea!' I knew Freddo was my first best friend for a reason.

We arranged to meet at my house after tea. Or

rather, Freddo and I arranged it and Gordon just nodded weakly. He didn't have the strength to argue.

Freddo came up trumps. He turned up with a pile of cardboard with pictures of awesome looking laptops printed on the side. It was the sort of rubbish that made my family look rich. In addition, he provided Gordon with an über-thick all-in-one wetsuit.

Gordon's strength had returned enough to squeeze himself into his brain and body protection outfit. He looked more like a police frogman than a forensic scientist. He couldn't bend his knees but he seemed to be happy enough with his new suit and waddled out into our street like a penguin.

Freddo brought eight CCTV cameras. The plan was to install them at every window and film the outside of the house. The images would be transmitted to the frogman's laptop. When we saw someone breaking in, we'd call the police. Simples!

Mum, Dad and Timmy had been invited to drinks with parents from Timmy's playgroup. Jessie was supposed to be keeping an eye on me but as usual her bedroom door was firmly shut so there was no one around to interfere with our plans.

The only problem was that I needed to get into

Jessie's room to set up the camera in her window overlooking the front garden. I knocked on the door to ask if I could come in.

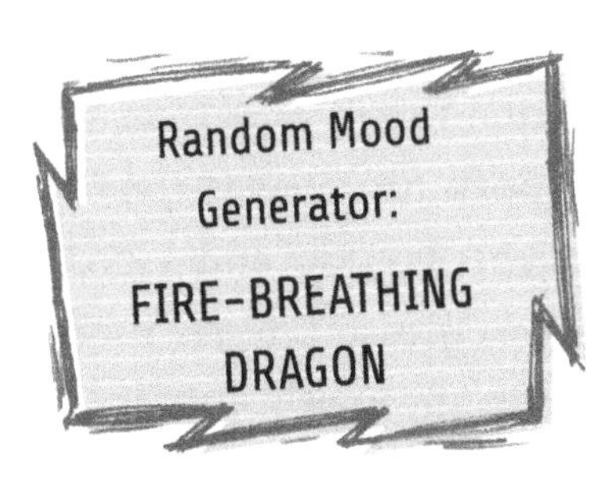


'Get out!' she roared. 'I don't want a thieving burglar anywhere near me.'

'Those pictures are a case of mistaken identity,' I said. 'It's easy to do. I mean, I thought you and Dazzer were the burglars. You were the ones outside in the middle of the night, after all.'

'Are you mad? Do you think we have any time to commit burglaries?'

'Too busy snogging?' I said.

'Yes, actually.' Jessie blushed.

That meant they didn't have the opportunity.

'Where do you get your money from to go bowling all the time?' I said.

'We don't go bowling. That's just what I tell

Mum. We just hang out.' Jessie blushed even more.

I believed her. Jessie would never pass a lie detection test. So she didn't have the motive to be a burglar either. She didn't need money. All that boyfriend-girlfriend stuff was free. Without means, motive and opportunity it was clear that Jessie was as innocent as me, Freddo and Gordon. I hated to admit it but I was pleased. Jessie might be the most annoying sister in the world but at least she wasn't a crook.

'You didn't do it,' I said. 'I didn't do it. So don't you think we better find out who did? This house is one of the very few houses round here that hasn't been broken into yet.'

'What do you think I can do about it?' Jessie said. 'I've been grounded unless you hadn't noticed, Sherlock Holmes.'

A fuzzy warm feeling bubbled up in my stomach. Jessie had never paid me such a compliment before. I liked being called Sherlock Holmes.

'Sherlock Holmes is the greatest fictional detective of all time, but I have a more modern approach: CCTV. We've laid a trap for them. If we see anyone coming near the house, we can take appropriate action.' I waggled the video camera at her.

Jessie's eyelids flickered as she thought about what I said. In the end she stood back and let me enter her room.

Once the cameras were set up, I went out to find Gordon and Freddo, who had set up surveillance HQ in the bus shelter, which was plastered with Wanted posters of the three of us and a picture of Mrs Brown's missing cat.

Freddo was wearing a blue curly wig, a green tartan jacket and pink jogging bottoms. He looked even weirder than Gordon the frogman.

'Reverse psychology,' he said.

'That's a big word for you,' I said.

'Actually it's two words, Mr Kendal,' Gordon said, which told me exactly where Freddo got the phrase from.

'If I look this crazy, no one will recognise me as the same guy in the e-fit pictures.'

'But you still have a packet of crisps in your hand.'

'These aren't crisps, they're cheese puffs.' He held up the packet of snacks.

'I'm not sure the suspicious neighbours will know the difference.'

Freddo shrugged.

I had totally overlooked the need for a different disguise. The whole point of dressing like a ninja, even an almost one, was that I could blend in with the shadows. Freddo wasn't blending in with anything.

'Any sign of movement yet?' I asked.

'Your parents just drove off,' Gordon said. 'And there is a cat wandering about.'

My heart jumped. A cat? The missing cat? The missing cat with a reward on its head?

'Which cat?'

'*Felis Catus*,' Gordon said. 'A very fluffy version.'

'This cat?' I pointed to the picture pasted to the wall of the bus shelter.

'Affirmative.' Gordon nodded curtly.

'One hundred pounds reward.' Freddo scratched his head under his wig.

'I'll split it with you if we catch it,' I said.

I needed the money to replace Gordon's night-vision goggles case. He had refused to bring the goggles out with him tonight without a case, which was annoying but understandable.

Freddo held up his hand and we high-fived.

'Ahem.' Gordon cleared his throat.

'You are allergic to cats,' Freddo said.

'I'm not allergic to a third of the reward,' Gordon said.

I couldn't argue with him even though I suspected that the goggles case would cost more than my share of the reward.

It was still too early for burglars so a frogman, Coco the clown and an almost-ninja followed the cat down Beechwood Road and into Beechwood Close, which is a dead end off our road.

There are only two houses in Beechwood Close – Dad said the builders ran out of money for more. The rest of the area is fenced off and the only thing living there is a family of foxes. But today, the fence had been moved and a VW campervan was parked up. It was the really cool type that every surf dude wants – bright orange and white with a shiny chrome bumper. But we lived miles from the sea. What was a surf dude's camper doing parked there?

The lights in the van were switched on and the smell of sizzling bacon wafted from an open window. The missing cat jumped up onto the generator that was humming outside and squeezed through the half-open window.

Freddo nudged me to take a look. Gordon stood well back, rocking from side to side as if he needed the toilet. I hoped he could hold it. There was no way he could rush home for the bathroom right now.

I crept up to the van and peered through the window.

The cat was rubbing itself around someone sitting on the sofa. And that person was glued to the TV screen playing Xbox.

Total result! We had found the missing cat AND the burglar. And even better, I recognised who it was.

# When Is a Burglar Not a Burglar?

I rushed back to Freddo and Gordon, who were hanging around at the entrance to the close.

'It's Victor!' I hissed. 'Victor Brown. He lives in our street. His house was burgled last. That's his mum's cat. It was his Xbox that was stolen and he's playing on it right now! It's definitely him. He used to babysit for us sometimes.'

'Then your mate Victor is a thief,' Freddo said.

Gordon didn't say a word, he was too busy studying his laptop.

'But why would he break into his own home and steal his own Xbox and cat?' I said.

Freddo shrugged.

'Do you think we should call the police?' I said. 'Tell them he is the burglar?'

'No way!' Freddo said. 'They'll recognise us from the e-fit pictures and will arrest us.'

'But if they don't know that Victor took his own Xbox, they'll still be looking for us. We can't go around dressed like this forever. Gordon will suffocate. You'll have to run away to the circus. I'll have to join a miserable punk band and wear eyeliner. Dad already thinks I'm a Goth.'

'There's nothing wrong with this wig,' Freddo said.

Gordon raised his eyebrows but carried on looking at his laptop through his deep-sea diver's mask. The argument ping-ponged back and forth between me and my best friend. Freddo can be very stubborn sometimes.

'I'm sorry to interrupt, Mr Kendal.' Gordon tapped me on the shoulder with his snorkel. 'But I think you need to direct the police elsewhere. According to your CCTV cameras, someone is trying to break into your home right now.'

'Burglars! My house! Right now!' I pushed Freddo out of the way and tried to snatch the laptop away from Gordon. But Gordon stabbed me with his snorkel.

'You can see but not touch,' he said.

'Show me the pictures!' I really didn't have time for Gordon's hang-ups.

Gordon tilted his laptop so I could see the screen.

Three figures in jeans and hoodies were in our back garden. There was a fourth person right below the camera, almost out of shot. He must have been trying to get in through the back door but Mum's new bolt was slowing him up.

The burglars weren't Jessie, Dazzer, Victor or us.

They were a gang of hard nuts I didn't know and they were at my house!

'Call the police!' I yelled.

Gordon typed 999 into his laptop and the sound of a phone ringing echoed through the empty night.

'Come on, come on!' I felt so helpless. The real burglars were burglarizing my house! Mum and Dad were out. Jessie was still inside. I didn't want her to be stolen. She was my sister, after all.

The phone seemed to ring forever.

'They've gone inside!' Freddo said. 'They'll be in and out in no time. These guys won't hang around.'

He was right. They were professionals.

'Come on then!' I grabbed Freddo's tartan sleeve. 'We've got to stop them ourselves.'

# The Almost-Ninja Goes to Work

Beechwood Road was quiet. A few houses had lights on behind drawn curtains. Number thirty-three, my home, was dark. Freddo and I hesitated at the front gate, trying to catch our breath.

'Front or back?' Freddo said.

'The front door's double locked,' I said. 'They won't be able to get out that way.'

'Let's go round the back then. Stop them leaving with your stuff.'

Gordon waddled up the street. 'The police are on their way. Expected time of arrival – fifteen minutes.'

'Fifteen minutes! They might be gone by then,' I said. 'Come on!'

I opened the side gate and we crept into the back garden. The back door stood wide open. Mum's new bolt hung twisted and broken on one screw.

Gordon still had his laptop open and I kept getting glimpses of us moving from camera to camera – the almost-ninja, the frogman and the clown. Three crazy detectives. But I didn't want to see us. I wanted to see the burglars. Why hadn't I set up any cameras in the house?

As we crept into the house, I stepped right into a bulging bag with a charity-store logo. The plastic rustled and something squeaked from inside. I winced, convinced the burglars would hear.

STOP!

REWIND!

What did Mum give to charity? Stuff she found lying around on the floor. My stuff!

I ripped open the bag to see if there was anything we could use against the burglars. It was all there. Jessie's My Little Pony collection, the remains of the Barker, my marbles and loads of mini pots of slime.

'Can you put this back together, Gordon?' I held up the Barker. 'Get the motion sensor to fire foam bullets again and the digital voice recorder to play?'

Gordon nodded. He shut the lid of his laptop so it was like a miniature table and started work at once.

'Freddo, these are for you.' I passed him a load of My Little Ponies.

Freddo looked confused. 'Do they fire pony poo?'

'No, but trust me – they are good missiles.'

Freddo nodded and shoved the ponies into the waistband of his jogging bottoms.

Gordon handed me the motion sensor Nerf gun and the voice recorder. I dangled the motion sensor round my neck and pocketed the voice recorder. The speakers were massive – I could only carry one but it didn't matter as I didn't need surround sound for what I had in mind.

'Gordon,' I said, 'go back to the road and flag down the police when they arrive.'

Gordon waddled away, his wetsuit squeaking as his legs rubbed together.

That left me and Freddo to defend my family home. I might not have been wearing the greatest disguise but I was pleased I was wearing all black. It made me almost feel like a ninja and I needed every boost I could get.

'Ready, Freddo?'

Freddo nodded his blue curly head. He looked ridiculous but he was the best friend and the best backup an almost-ninja could have.

I gave him a thumbs up and stepped into the utility room.

I didn't need night-vision goggles. This was my home. I knew my way around in the dark.

First I noticed my school bag and all my school stuff was dumped on the floor. The burglars had rejected my homework! I'd worked for hours on those worksheets and what was wrong with my awesome pencil case? Even the burglars thought me and my stuff was a worthless load of zilch, nada, zero.

I stepped over my bag and crept into the hall. Freddo panted cheese and onion heavily behind me. I hoped the burglars wouldn't smell us coming.

Noises came from the sitting room. One of the burglars was in there, probably choosing their favourite DVDs to steal.

Freddo mimed throwing pony missiles through the sitting-room door. I shook my head. I didn't want to scare the burglars off, I wanted to catch them. Plus, if they ran away, they might take the

DVDs with them and I hadn't seen *Iron Man 3* yet.

I needed to set a trap.

Dad had confiscated my skateboard, but he'd only shoved it in the cupboard under the stairs. I took it out and lined it up perfectly between the sitting-room door and the open cupboard door.

I mimed a few actions to Freddo. He nodded and gave me a thumbs up.

Burglar number one – sorted.

*Click – fizz!* Someone was opening a can in the kitchen. Mum doesn't let us have fizzy drinks except at Christmas, so the only cans in the fridge were Dad's beer. He'd go mental when he saw one had been nicked. He might even blame me! I couldn't let the burglar get away with it.

I loaded the motion-sensor shooter with foam bullets and placed it on the floor with the laser beam across the kitchen doorway. The moment the burglar left the kitchen, they would be bombarded with foam bullets. I was hoping they'd be too shocked to know they were only getting hit with a toy. They'd drop the beer and panic.

Burglar number two – sorted.

Upstairs, the floorboards creaked. The other

burglars were in Mum and Dad's room by the sound of it.

'I'll flush them out. I want them to come downstairs,' I murmured to Freddo. 'You get ready to attack.'

He nodded and hid himself behind the curtain at the front door, a pony in each hand.

I scattered my killer marbles on the stairs.

That left me with the mini slime pots. I prised the lids off and lined them up on the table in the hall.

'Ready?' I whispered to Freddo.

A smell wafted out from behind the curtain which I took to be a 'yes'.

The time had come to put my latest plan into action.

I plugged the digital voice recorder into the speaker and pressed the red button.

'*WHO LET THE DOGS OUT? WOOF! WOOF! WOOF! WOOF!*' Freddo's favourite song blasted through the house.

A number of things happened at once.

The sitting-room door flew open and burglar number one rushed out. She stepped on the skateboard, which shot along at supersonic speed.

She flapped her arms and wailed like a seagull, but nothing could stop her hurtling straight into the cupboard under the stairs. I slammed the door shut.

Result!

Upstairs the burglars rushed out of Mum and Dad's room at exactly the same time as a wailing banshee erupted from Jessie's bedroom.

Jessie was so bored she had been trying out beauty treatments. Her latest face mask looked terrifying.

The burglars screamed when they saw her.

Jessie screamed when she saw them.

The burglars ran downstairs towards me and Freddo, only they weren't running on carpet, they were running on marbles. One came down the stairs head first, the other feet first. They landed in a groaning heap at the bottom of the stairs.

Burglars two and three, sorted.

The last burglar came out of the kitchen with Dad's lager in his hand. He had earphones plugged in. Jessie's earphones. It sounded like tinny mosquitoes playing One Dimension, but he must have had it up full volume because he couldn't hear the Barker. Freddo flung a turquoise and purple

My Little Pony at him. It hit him on the head and rebounded straight into the laser beam. A volley of foam bullets let rip.

The guy suddenly realised he was busted and ran towards the utility room, but I wasn't going to let him get away. I slung a fistful of bright green slime right in his face. He dropped his can of lager and staggered around with his arms outstretched like a blind zombie. Served him right for drinking Dad's beer.

Jessie stormed down the stairs. I don't know who looked more crazy, her or Freddo. Her face was plastered with face pack and her hair stuck out in all directions like the Statue of Liberty. She trampled over the burglars at the bottom of the stairs as if they were doormats and went straight up to Slime Eyes.

'That's mine!' She snatched the earphones out of his ears. 'And so is that!' She snatched her phone back. 'Now, get out of my house!' She grabbed him and shoved him through the utility room towards the back door.

The burglar stumbled over my maths books, but recovered and tried to sprint through the back door.

'Don't let him get away!' I shouted.

I could just see a small frogman standing on the

patio. He twirled the snorkel round his head and threw it.

The snorkel struck the burglar right in the face and he slumped to the ground.

'You're the man, Gordon!' I whooped.

'Who let the dogs out?' Freddo shouted and did a weird dance.

For the first time in her entire life, Jessie didn't know what to say. She looked from me, to Gordon, to Freddo, and to each of the burglars in turn.

'We caught the burglars!' I said.

Jessie smiled and great chunks of face mask fell off her cheeks.

'Nice one, bro!' she said and held her hand up for a high five. We slapped hands like true friends.

'High five!' Freddo said and held his hand up too.

Jessie hesitated for a second then slapped his hand away. Jessie had never been so friendly with Freddo, but I noticed she wiped her hand on her dressing gown when he wasn't looking.

'High five!' Gordon squeaked and held his hand up but he changed his mind and dropped it again, giggling shyly.

Jessie snorted and shoved her hands in her pockets.

Poor Gordon! He had taken out the last burglar. He was as much a hero as everyone else.

'High five, Gordon!' I said. As I reached out to slap his hand, Gordon grabbed mine and squeezed it. I grabbed Freddo and the three detectives joined hands and held them high.

# Heroes Not Zeroes

The house was full of semi-conscious burglars when the police turned up a few minutes later. Six fully loaded squad cars, two motorbikes, and a van. Beechwood Road looked like the place to be.

Four police officers charged down the side alley and grabbed me, Freddo, Jessie and Gordon.

'It's not us!' I said.

Jessie and Freddo shouted something similar but Gordon was too traumatised to speak and could only wail. I don't think a stranger had touched him in a very long time. Even a seven-millimetre thick neoprene wetsuit couldn't protect him.

Inspector Locke shuffled over to us. 'Let them go,

team. These aren't our burglars. But these are.'

It turned out the burglars were a gang of sixth formers from the posh school up the road. They had all been expelled for smoking so their parents had grounded them, confiscated their phones and stopped their allowances. But unlike Jessie, these hard nuts didn't stay in their room painting their

nails until their punishment was over – they'd decided to steal the stuff they wanted from other people. Us and all our neighbours.

The police were delighted that we had caught the burglars breaking in on camera. Gordon had saved the CCTV footage to the Cloud, but the forensic team still invaded our house later to collect evidence, but they weren't dressed in paper onesies and carrying silver cases like Gordon. I don't think they watched *CSI*.

'Do you want to go and see what they are doing, Gordon?' I asked. 'You might learn something.'

Gordon scowled.

'I mean, teach them something,' I quickly corrected myself.

'No, thank you,' Gordon said. 'I think I'll wait until I'm eighteen to join the police force.'

Mum and Dad didn't know what to say when they came home to find four burglars being bundled into the back of a police van. They were a mixture of horrified, proud, shocked and impressed. Timmy loved all the police vehicles and insisted on looking in every single one even though it was well past his bedtime.

While we watched the police go about their work, Mrs Brown came over to talk to Dad.

'I need your advice, Mr Kendal,' Mrs Brown said to Dad. 'It's about Victor and his Xbox.'

'Victor is in the caravan round the corner,' I said.

'I know. He rang and told me this evening,' Mrs Brown said. 'That's the problem. He came to the house the other day without me knowing and took his own Xbox. He's run away from university. He's been living in the caravan with the cat. Oh, dear! I feel such a fool. I don't know what to say to the police.'

'They won't mind,' Dad said. 'They'll be pleased that they can knock one thing off their list. They're busy enough.'

'Busy taking over our house,' Jessie said. 'I need to use the bathroom, and I'm not going in there with a bunch of strangers around.' She picked pieces of face mask off her cheeks.

Mum had tears in her eyes. I'm not sure if it was because she was proud of the middle child she normally forgot about or whether she had been slicing onions at the drinks party.

'Great work, Dan!' Mum said. 'You solved the crime of the century. I really think you deserve a reward. What do you want?'

'Can I have my skateboard back?'

'Sure,' said Dad. 'Though it took quite a beating with that burglar . . . How would you like a brand-new one?' Dad said.

'Yes, please! Can we take Freddo to the skate shop to help me choose?'

'Sure thing.' Dad reached up and patted my shoulder.

'One more thing . . .' I whispered something in Dad's ear.

Dad nodded and whispered something in Mum's ear.

Mum nodded.

'Jessie?' Dad said. 'I understand you helped the

boys. Well done. And thank you for not sneaking out behind our backs while we were at the party.'

Jessie shrugged. 'I'm grounded.'

'You can consider yourself ungrounded. Would you like to invite Dazzer round for tea tomorrow?' Dad said.

'If you like.' Jessie pretended not to be that bothered but I saw the edge of her mouth twitch slightly as if she was trying to hide a smile.

'Let's invite everyone,' Mum said. 'We can have a party.'

'Will there be crisps?' Freddo asked.

'Of course,' Mum said. 'What's your favourite food, Gordon?'

'I'll bring my own,' Gordon whispered, still in shock from nearly being arrested.

'Do you mind having a joint party, Jessie?' I asked. 'My friends and yours?'

'It'll be cool,' Jessie said. 'You guys are heroes. But do you think they could wear some normal clothes?'

Amazeballs! I had been promoted from zero to hero! But I think Jessie was going to be disappointed. Freddo was never going to take that wig off.

'It's all yours now,' Inspector Locke said as the forensic team trooped out of our house. 'The burglars made quite a mess, I'm afraid, Mrs Kendal. And there is fingerprint dust everywhere but it is easily removed with soap and water.'

'I don't mind,' Mum said. 'The whole family will work together to get our home back to normal. We can have a clear-out while we are at it. You'll help, won't you, Dan?'

'Heroes don't do housework,' I told her quickly. 'And anyway I need to speak to Mr Elson first.' There was one more crime that needed clearing up and I had all the evidence he needed.

# 21 The Anonymous Dog Poo Detective

Mr Elson loved my footage of the werepoodle so much I was sure he was going to pay me double the reward.

'Brilliant work, Daniel. Just brilliant.' Mr Elson jumped up and down like Timmy does when he's had too much chocolate. 'This is the proof that I needed.'

'You said something about a reward,' I said hopefully. Mum and Dad were going to buy me a new skateboard but I still had to replace Gordon's night-vision goggles case.

'A reward?' Mr Elson looked at me blankly. 'Of course. Right now I'm going to phone the police. Report this mutt.'

'It's not Lucy's fault – Mr and Mrs Gonzales are the ones who haven't been clearing up after her.' I'd only shown Mr Elson the stills from the video to get the reward, but Lucy was just a silly little dog. She'd be miserable in doggy jail. 'Are you sure you want to call the police? Mr and Mrs Gonzales are our new neighbours and they are coming to the party we're having later. You're coming too, aren't you?' I said, hoping he'd get my point. Mum wouldn't want an argument to break out at the celebration.

Mr Elson frowned as if he was thinking hard.

'Maybe you are right. But what are we going to do? I'm totally fed up with the mess on the pavement but I don't want to fall out with our new neighbours.'

'I think we should handle this anonymously,' I said. 'Can I use your printer?'

There was such a large crowd of neighbours outside our house admiring the police cars, that no one noticed an almost-ninja and an elderly gentleman sneak up the nearby path and slip a photo through Lucy's owners' letter box.

'Let's hope they take the hint,' Mr Elson said.

'Nice working with you, Daniel. Here's your reward.' He handed me a bundle of new ten-pound notes.

Hooray! I was going to be able to replace Gordon's case and still have some left over for stickers for my new skateboard.

Mum and Dad invited so many people to the party, including the police and the full forensic team, that there wasn't going to be enough room for everyone in our house, so we changed the celebration to a street party.

All our neighbours lined up their garden furniture and gazebos down the centre of the street. Mr Elson blasted ancient grown-up music through speakers he placed on his front doorstep and some people danced. There was loads of food and so many crisps Freddo thought he was in heaven. Gordon bought his own camping chair and a plastic box with an anaemic sandwich. I think he must disinfect his food as well as everything else because the sandwich looked like it had been bleached.

It was a brilliant party and suddenly Beechwood Road seemed like a community I wanted to be part of. I wasn't going to need to run away to the circus after all.

The anonymous tip off worked brilliantly. There were no arguments and no more dog poo.

'Shall we call ourselves the Dog Poo Detectives from now on?' I asked Freddo and Gordon during the party.

Freddo couldn't answer because his mouth was crammed with crisps.

'No way, Mr Kendal.' Gordon's eyeballs started pulsing again. 'I prefer to stay anonymous.'

'Okay then, how about the Anonymous Detectives?'

Gordon put his eyeballs away and held up his hand for a rare high five.

'The Anonymous Detectives strike again!' he squeaked and slapped my hand like a true friend.

Don't miss Dan's other escapades!

## Help! I'm an Alien

Daniel can't help but see the differences between him and his family. Big sister Jessie explains that Daniel is in fact an alien, kindly adopted by her parents. Confused, Daniel turns to his best friends, Freddo and Gordon the Geek, for help. Together perhaps they can work out where he really belongs!

## Help! I'm a Genius

Daniel isn't a genius like the rest of his family and he certainly isn't a brainiac like Gordon the Geek. So when there is a quiz to represent the school in a national competition he knows he will not be selected. However Daniel is wrong about most things, will he be right this time?